HYPOALLERGENIC DIET

A Complete Guide

Includes Diet Rationale, Shopping Tips, & Over 100 Delicious Easy To Make Recipes

Saeid Mushtagh B.Sc., Naturopathic Doctor

Foreword By Dr. Wayne Steinke B.Sc., N.D.

Saeid Mushtagh
2006, Toronto

The instructions of this book are intended to complement naturopathic medical approaches to health and healing. The health claims are relative to one's individual health status and medical history.

The suggested diet protocols are subject to change by Naturopathic or Medical Doctors for specific conditions, as well as for case history, and management requirements.

Design by Saeid Mushtagh

Catalogue in publication
Mushtagh, Saeid, 2006
     Hypoallergenic Diet A Complete Guide:
     Foreword by Wayne Steinke—1st ed.
Includes index
ISBN 0-9780690-0-5

1. Hypoallergenic Diet I. Title

Printed and bound in Canada by Hignell Printing Ltd.

To my teachers,
at the Canadian College of Naturopathic Medicine, Toronto,
to whom I extend my deepest gratitude.

Acknowledgement

This book would not have been possible without the constant encouragement and support of my colleagues and friends. I would like to acknowledge Dr. Wayne Steinke for his mentorship, without his inspiration this project would never have started. I wish to extend my gratitude to Dr. Steinke, Dr. Jonathon Prousky, and Dr. Iva Lloyd for reviewing and providing invaluable comments on the manuscript. I also extend my thanks to Dr. Neil Tran for being a constant encouragement and for the initial proof reading and editing of the manuscript, to Dr. Maggie Thibodeau for proofreading the manuscript, to Dr. Jolene Kennett for helping with preparation of recipes and editing the instructions, to Mr. Perry Au at Hignell Printing for his professional advise and assistance with printing the book. Finally, I wish to thank my friends at CCNM for inspiring me and enjoying the recipes.

Table Of Contents

Table Of Contents

Foreword

In a time where rates of chronic disease and health costs have risen to never before seen highs, it seems apparent that new paradigms are needed to take health care into this new millennium. But, it is a narrow path we navigate in determining what aspects of the old are based on truth, and which are based only upon relative realities. What do we build upon as a basic foundation and what do we delegate to relative obscurity?

The first step in improving upon a practice or a philosophy is acknowledging that there is a need to do so and that growth and change are a natural part of existence. The existing "Health Care System" as based upon allopathic principles has many functional ways and means, but it has far from reached its potential. It would be more aptly named the "Disease Care System" as it truly is focused on the treatment of disease, not on the ideals (physical, mental, & spiritual/emotional) of individual health. There are many asymptomatic people who are far from healthy.

Medicine is not a science as is popularly believed. The practice of medicine is based upon science and it is slowly moving in that direction, but in the strictest sense of what we know and understand about health, it is far from being absolute and reproducible. Indeed, the linear, reductionist ideals which are the foundations for physical sciences like physics and chemistry are wholly inadequate to describe living dynamic systems. For principles pertaining to living, dynamic systems which allow for balance, imbalance, change, relativity, and reproducibility, we need only to look to nature itself and ecology. After all, is the human body not simply a microcosm of the macrocosm?

There is not one specific diet out there suitable to all individuals and their specific needs. When you account for both internal and external factors, of a physical, mental, and spiritual/emotional nature we can begin to account for the beautiful diversity which is a human being. That which is living and healthy is not static but rather dynamic. It is constructive not destructive. There are general principles which can be ascribed to a balanced, healthy, constructive system. Principles which support life as we know it, which maximize your genetics, and help bring balance to that which is your body, your mind and your feelings. For example, we do not ideally say that "sugar is bad" and create a dualistic law which some people buy into and some don't, thus bringing more conflict to the world. Rather, it is truer

i

to state a principle that "refined carbohydrate (sugar) devoid of vitamins, minerals, enzymes and an assortment of other co-factors are usually metabolically unbalancing to a human body and are more destructive in their effects than constructive".

This book is a much overdue work. It empowers the reader with timeless principles based on Naturopathic traditions. It is based on health, so it holds the potential to help you heal yourself, no matter what your condition. Life is not about supplements or medications. Life is about doing and Being. A hypoallergenic elimination diet is one of the best ways for people to give their body a break. When done in conjunction with some lifestyle modifications, people are often amazed by how quickly their bodies begin to rid themselves of a variety of "dis-ease" states.

I believe that Dr. Mushtagh successfully explains enough of the basic principles pertaining to elimination and cleansing that most anyone reading them must contemplate their logic and potential. To people who are ever skeptical? Good I say. I challenge you to keep an open mind, put on hold the criticism of the ignorant and try things first hand so that empirically you may come to your own conclusions.

Sincerely,
Dr. Wayne Steinke B.Sc., N.D.
April 4, 2006

Preface

The idea for this book emerged when I was treating a patient with Irritable Bowel Syndrome. After two weeks on the hypoallergenic diet, the patient reported a 40% reduction in diarrhea and abdominal bloating. She also felt calmer and less anxious about her bowel movements. In spite of the obvious success, this patient said that she could not continue with the diet. When asked what she was eating during the day, it became clear that she was not snacking anymore, and her usual lunch of a fast-food sandwich was now reduced to nothing. She reported feeling constantly hungry because she did not know what else she could eat! To ensure continued success, it was necessary to immediately provide her with recipes and snack options, which she tried and loved and was much better on the next visit.

Her plight helped me realize that as a naturopathic doctor in training I had been introduced to many food alternatives such that I did not recognize the restrictiveness of the diet that my patient experienced. The problem that I faced was that the general public did not seem to know how to prepare simple (or even more complex) meals and snacks that fit within the diet guidelines. For this reason my patient experienced the sense that her food choices were extremely restricted.

As a result of the above incident, it became a common practice to provide recipes to all patients who were following the hypoallergenic diet and refer them to alternative cookbooks. A second problem became apparent at this point; there were no cookbooks that specifically featured the hypoallergenic diet. There were books with gluten and/or dairy free recipes. However, resources were sparse when one searched for recipes that eliminated dairy, wheat, eggs, beef, pork, tomatoes, potatoes, citrus, sugar, and caffeine, to name a few examples.

This book is intended to serve as a methodical yet simple guide for the Hypoallergenic Diet. My hope is that the reader, my colleagues and their patients will find it a useful resource for embarking on the journey towards health.

Sincerely,
Saeid Mushtagh B.Sc., Naturopathic Doctor
May 6, 2006

Part 1
Rationale Behind
The Hypoallergenic Diet

Digestion, The Basics

Food must be broken down into its basic components before it can be absorbed in the intestines. For example, proteins become amino acids when broken down, starch and complex carbohydrates become simple carbohydrate units, and complex fats become fatty acids and glycyrides. This process is known as digestion.

Digestion happens in the Gastrointestinal (GI) tract. The GI tract is a continuum composed of the mouth and esophagus, the stomach, and the small and large intestines. Digestion begins in the mouth through the act of mastication, and continues in the stomach, small intestine and large intestine.

The inner lining of GI tract is made off a special layer of cells known as the *mucosa*. The GI mucosa functions to regulate proper digestion and absorption of nutrients.

In the stomach, the main function of mucosa is to produce hydrochloric acid. Stomach acid helps with the break down of food products, as well as killing any microbes that enter the GI system.

After the stomach, the food enters the small intestine. Here the gall bladder releases bile into the small intestine. Bile is a yellow-green detergent like fluid that is made by the liver, stored in the gallbladder, and contains bile salts for fat digestion. Bile salts help break up fat into smaller particles. The pancreas, also releases digestive *enzymes* into the small intestine. Pancreatic enzymes are proteins that facilitate digestion of food particles. Enzymes needed for the final steps in digestion of proteins, carbohydrates and fats are found on the mucosal cells of the small intestine.

In the small intestine, where most of the absorption happens, the mucosa also acts as the site of absorption. The mucosal cells in the small intestine have extensions called the villi (pronounced vi-lai), and these villi have smaller extensions, called microvilli. Microvilli are the primary site of absorption of food particles. (See figure on page 4). Digested food particles are transported via specialized channels on the microvilli into the mucosal cells and then into the blood stream. Water and smaller minerals and vitamins will diffuse through the microvilli and directly enter the blood circulation.

The function of GI mucosa is under close regulation by the nervous system. The number of nerves controlling GI functions is so great that the gastrointestinal nervous system is often called the 'second brain'.

The nervous system function is necessary for proper release of stomach acid, bile, pancreatic and digestive enzymes, as well as the mechanical forces contributing to digestions, peristalsis (the churning movement of stomach and the intestines), and sufficient blood flow to the intestine for the absorption of nutrients.

The nervous system has two functional divisions: the *parasympathetic* nervous system and the *sympathetic* nervous system. These two divisions have opposing actions. The sympathetic portion controls the stress response. It is the remnants of the primitive man's fight/flight nervous system and functions primarily for survival. When this system is activated, the parasympathetic system shuts down. Blood is then shunted away from the digestive organs and sent into the muscles to literally enable the individual to run away from predators and to safety, or to stand the ground and fight. The parasympathetic part of the nervous system is responsible for more relaxed functions such as digestion, rest, repair, and reproduction.

Digestion is halted under sympathetic activation, and only resumes under relaxed conditions favored by parasympathetic activation.

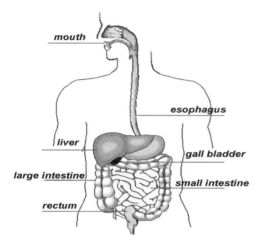

Gastrointestinal Tract

The GI tract is a continuum composed of the mouth, esophagus, the stomach, and the small and large intestines.

Cross Section of Small Intestine

The mucosal cells in the small intestine have functional extensions called the villi, and these villi have microvilli on them to enhance the absorption. Microvilli are the primary site of absorption of food particles.

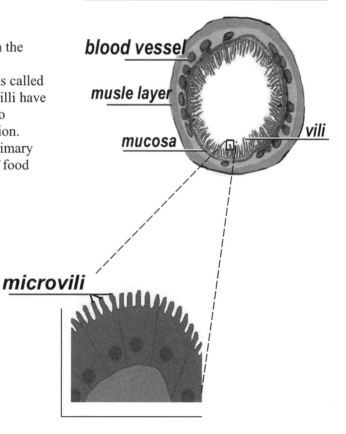

The Hypoallergenic Diet, An Overview

Medical sciences agree that individuals are widely different with respect to the enzymes and physiological pathways in the body, and these differences are significant in relation to metabolism and disease. No two individuals are the same. Therefore it is critical to have an understanding of foods and portions of food that suit your individual body and genetic make up. By following a diet that best suits your body, health can be restored, with an increased feeling of vitality and energy.

Most individuals have one or more food items that they are allergic or sensitive to and that their body does not function well on those foods. The reason simply being that their genetics and enzyme pathways are not selected to digest those foods properly. Just think of the foods that you dislike. The reason you don't like them can be that they don't sit well with your senses; they either don't smell right, don't taste right, or don't sit well with your stomach. This dislike is a natural faculty or a sense. With the onslaught of processed foods and complex packaged foods the body loses this natural sense, and this inherent ability to discriminate foods that do not suit the individual's genetic make up is lost. Hypoallergenic diet is a tool that will bring awareness to this inherent faculty, and will outline the foods that are causing your chronic symptoms. By making a few basic modifications to your diet and removing those foods you can then take charge of your health; no medication, no complicated treatments, or costly tests. Simply adjusting your diet.

In a healthy state the gastrointestinal system is able to digest and extract nutrients from the foods you eat and eliminate what it doesn't need as waste. Over time and through introduction of processed and packaged foods and unbalanced food choices that don't match your enzymatic make up, the digestive system becomes damaged and cannot function optimally. A damaged gastrointestinal system allows waste and undigested food particles to enter the body, which in turn causes allergies and sensitivities to many food items.

Food allergies are well-recognized in clinical medicine as a cause of acute attacks of asthma, anaphylaxis and skin eruptions, as well as a contributing factor in some cases of skin rashes, eczema and rhinitis (runny nose). These types of allergic reactions are controlled by the immune system. The immune system uses *antibodies* (protein complexes used by the immune system) to attack any foreign material in the body. For example in common seasonal allergies the immune system produces antibodies against flower pollens that enter the nostrils, which results in an immune reaction followed by inflammation causing hay fever and runny nose.

The antibodies involved in food allergic reactions are known as IgE and IgG antibodies. Presence of IgG and IgE antibodies can usually be detected thorough blood allergy testing or special skin scratch testing.

Allergic reactions and antibodies are also part of the cause in diseases with an autoimmune etiology, such as acne, psoriasis, gout, dermatitis, eczema, asthma, migraine, chronic rhinitis, arthritis and systemic lupus erythematosus (SLE)

A more subtle manifestation of food allergies is often referred to as 'food sensitivity'. Food sensitivities are common triggering factors for a wide range of physical and emotional disorders. Food sensitivities don't involve responses from the immune system. They are rather mediated by physiological responses to the offending foods, and are undetectable by blood work or skin scratch tests. These physiological responses include slow digestion, capillary and vessel contractions and lymphatic congestion. According to different sources, as many as sixty percent of the population suffers from undetected food sensitivities.

Symptoms of food sensitivities are varied. Most commonly they involve gastrointestinal symptoms. These gastrointestinal symptoms include any of basic symptoms such as bloating, gas, abdominal pain and discomfort, nausea and heartburn, as well as full blown gastrointestinal pathologies such as Crohn's, Ulcerative colitis, and Irritable Bowel Syndrome (IBS). These symptoms are the body's methods of communicating problems in the GI tract.

When gastrointestinal symptoms remain untreated for a period of time they can result in other group of symptoms such as recurrent ear infection, chronic muscle ache and pains, premenstrual syndrome, chronic fatigue, low energy, high blood pressure, and mood disorders. There is even research connecting food sensitivities to Attentions Deficit Disorder (ADD) and Attention Deficit Hyperactivity Disorder (ADHD).

It is often difficult to identify food allergies and sensitivities. Unlike the more obvious immediate immune reaction that can trigger anaphylaxis or hives, other food allergies and food sensitivity reactions will frequently be delayed by many hours or even several days. In general blood works can detect presence of food allergies only if the food had been consumed within seven days prior to the test. Also blood works are useless as far as food sensitivities go since the immune system doesn't make any antibodies in the case of sensitivities. Identifying a cause-effect relationship between specific foods and symptoms is further complicated by the tendency of people to crave the very foods to which they are allergic or sensitive.

The hypoallergenic diet is a well-planned and proven program that will aid you in identifying food allergies and sensitivities. The diet begins by eliminating the most common foods that are proven causes of allergies and sensitivities in the North American diet. Elimination of these foods will result in a general feeling of wellness and an increase in overall energy.

Once the symptoms have been reduced and gastrointestinal system has had sufficient time to heal, the eliminated foods are reintroduced into the diet one item at the time. This reintroduction will underline the specific foods that were the cause of allergies or sensitivities in your case. By restricting these underlined foods from your daily diet you then take charge of your gastrointestinal health and your symptoms

It is simple to follow a hypoallergenic diet program. But it requires some preparation and planning. You will find a pronounced effect when following the diet under the supervision of a trained Naturopathic or Medical Doctor, since your doctor can modify the length of the diet and restrict or expand the eliminated food lists to reflect your specific needs and condition. Also many doctors use adjunct therapies and supplements to facilitate the healing of the GI tract and this may be necessary given the medical history, specific symptoms, and the extent of gastro-intestinal damage.

Alternative Methods Of Identifying Food Allergies

There are specialized blood tests that are useful in diagnosis of food allergies. These test are expensive but they are valuable tools, and when indicated, are indispensable to your doctor.

One of these tests is an immunoglobulin assay, called ELISA. An immunoglobulin assay is testing blood for the presence of antibodies (IgG, and IgE) and immune reactions towards specific foods. The test has the potential of testing up to 240 food groups, and the number of food groups is increasing everyday as new methods are being developed.

A second useful test is cellular immune food reaction test, also know as Delayed-type Hypersensitivity Reaction (DHT) or Activated Cell Test (act). This is a less common blood test valuable in detecting delayed allergies not caught by the ELISA. This test looks at a part of the immune system's responce to food that can be delayed up to 3 days after eating the foods.

Some labs combine these tests into a very comprehensive test known as ELIS/ACT test.

The downfall of these lab tests is that they can only pick up frank allergies where there is an immune reaction and antibody formation. This means food sensitivities, which don't involve antibodies, cannot be identified on these test. Therefore when there are certain food sensitivities that cause abnormal physiological responses, such as slow digestion, fluid and lymph congestion, and small blood vessel and capillary contraction, these tests cannot identify the problem causing foods.

Compared to these labs tests the advantage of the hypoallergenic diet is that it is an economical approach that underlines food allergies as well as food sensitivities.

Gastrointestinal Health And Food Sensitivity

The complete mechanism of action for food sensitivities and allergies remains to be fully elucidated. There are, however, a number of findings and sound hypotheses that offer explanations. Ultimately, all these explanations point to an unhealthy damaged gastrointestinal mucosa as the culprit in food sensitivities.

Food allergies and sensitivities begin when undigested food particles, mainly proteins, bypass damaged mucosa and enter the blood circulation. In general, there are two contributing factors that damage the mucosa and result in undigested food particles.

The first contributing factor is the habitual consumption of packaged and processed foods. These are foods that are not easily digested and put an extra demand on the available digestive enzymes and mechanical digestion. Excessive consumption of these foods will dampen the ability of the GI system and the digestive enzymes to properly digest foods. The undigested food particles act much like sandpaper rubbing against the microvilli and creating micro-tears on the mucosa.

The second contributing factor leading to damaged mucosa is improper digestion of food due to stress. Stress responses (fight/flight responses) stimulate the sympathetic nervous system. Excessive stress or anxiety during the day, improper rest, eating on the go, too much work and too little play, and other sources of emotional stresses combine together to compromise digestion by over stimulating the sympathetic nervous system at the expense of parasympathetic nervous system.

In our modern society where such immediate external factors such as predators are replaced by day-to-day stress responses (responses to deadlines, traffic, an unaccommodating boss, exams, or even a simple task as driving), it has become the norm to spend most of the day in a sympathetic (fight or flight) mode. When one functions on a sympathetic state, the parasympathetic system is shut down. As a result of stress, stomach acid and digestive enzymes are decreased and peristalsis is halted leading to inadequate digestion of foods in the digestive system.

Damages to the mucosa is a normal part of the mucosal life cycle, and the body has the ability to heal the micro-tears. But stress complicates things further, since under chronic stress, the body's ability to heal the micro-tears is also halted. Recall that the parasympathetic nervous system, which is shut down under stress, regulates all the healing functions of the body.

The net result of poorly digested foods in the intestinal lumen is development of an unhealthy mucosa that bears many micro-tears. This is a volatile situation, since undigested food particles can escape the intestinal lumen via these micro-tears and enter the blood circulation. Once in the circulation, these partially digested food particles, especially the undigested proteins, will cause physiological and autoimmune manifestations responsible for many chronic diseases such as gastrointestinal upsets, gas, bloating and heart burn, arthritis, high blood pressure and so on.

There is a gastrointestinal condition known as the Leaky Gut Syndrome. Individuals with this disease have small gaps in between the cells of their mucosa that allow the partially digested food into the circulation. Leaky Gut Syndrome is the extreme end of the spectrum in terms of damaged mucosa. The milder form of damage is a gastrointestinal tract in which the cell-to-cell connections are intact, but food particles are not properly digested and mucosa bears micro-tears.

The next few sections will explore the adverse effects which undigested food proteins can have once they enter the circulation via the micro-tears.

Autoimmune Manifestations Of Food Allergies

The immune system is designed to recognize and attack any foreign proteins that enter the body. This will ensure the recognition of viruses and bacteria that have different protein coats. At the same time the immune system has a way of recognizing the body's own healthy cells. Each cell for example has a particular protein tag on its membrane, allowing it to be recognized and avoid attack by the immune cells.

Partially digested food proteins that enter the circulation end up precipitating in different locations in the body. They are recognized by the immune system as foreign proteins, otherwise known as antigen.

The immune system mounts an immune response against these foreign proteins. These immune responses involve local inflammation and antibody production (IgG, IgE). Inflammation is designed to increase circulation to the tissue and bring other immune cells to the area to attack and clear the foreign proteins. The antibodies are deigned to bind to and clear the foreign proteins. But inflammation is not a precisely targeted mechanism and it often influences the surrounding tissue. Therefore the inflammation mounted against the undigested food proteins damages otherwise healthy tissues.

Depending on the location of the immune response, the exact nature and shape of these undigested proteins, the tissues they precipitate in, and the shape of the IgG antibody, the inflammation can cause different symptoms. If these food proteins are within joint capsules, or resemble the shape of some human protein in the joint capsule, for example, one will have arthritis-like symptoms. If the undigested proteins are within the blood vessels that deliver blood to the brain, headaches and migraines occur as a result of blood vessel spasm. If these food antigens are similar to skin proteins or have an affinity for the skin tissue, then acne, generalized rashes, eczema, and psoriasis are common findings. These are the common symptoms, but the list goes on.

During the course of the hypoallergenic diet, the body will get a chance gently cleanse the system from the food proteins. As the result inflammation subsides and the affected tissues heal.

Large Intestinal Flora And Food Sensitivity

Another reason for the effectiveness of hypoallergenic diet is its normalizing effect on the micro-flora of the large intestine.

About one third of digestion is done in the large intestine. This part of digestion is done by the billions of bacteria (micro-flora) living in the large intestine. These bacteria are varied in kind. They are a normal part of the intestinal system. Each bacterial kind has different enzymes that allow it to digest certain foods. The delicate balance between the number of each kind is crucial for proper digestion of proteins, fats, cholesterol, organic acids, etc.[1]

Undigested food proteins serve as energy sources for certain kinds of bacteria and favor the growth of these bacteria over the others. This favored growth will shifts the bacterial balance in the large intestine at the determent of food digestion.

Certain food sensitivities tend to shift the balance in favor of the bacteria that are implicated in autoimmune reactions. Unbalanced growth of these bacteria activates the immune system. The immune system produces anti-bodies to kill and decrease the number of these bacteria. The problem is that proteins on the cell walls of these bacteria have a similar resemblance to human cells. Therefore the immune complexes that are meant to kill the overgrowing bacteria, once they enter the circulation, will cause inflammation and damage otherwise healthy tissue.

---

[1] Probiotic supplements are products that contain bacteria that are part of the healthy large intestine. Depending on your condition and the extent of imbalance, you may need probiotic supplementation as an adjunct to hypoallergenic diet. Before deciding on a probiotic supplement make sure to consult your naturopathic doctor. Many brands fail to deliver claimed amounts on the labels. Some may even be contaminated by unhealthy bacteria. Also many probiotic brands provide only a few kinds of bacteria. For example Lactobacillus Acidophilus supplement (the bacteria that grows in yogurt and breaks down lactose/milk sugar) is a very popular supplement. This is the first kind of bacteria to grow in the large intestine and begins populating the large intestine at infancy where there is a great need for digesting lactose. Lactobacillus however is only a small representative of the whole spectrum of the bacteria in an adult's large intestine.

The hypoallergenic diet has the effect of reestablishing the delicate balance in favor of a decreased autoimmune reaction and proper balance of bacterial kinds. The evidence for this comes from a 13 month randomized, placebo controlled trial of 53 patients with active rheumatoid arthritis. In this study, it was found that 12 of 27 patients in the treatment group, who all went through the hypoallergenic diet, had significantly improved symptoms of arthritic pain. In addition to the improvements in pain, the 12 patients also exhibited altered bacterial make up of their stool in favor of decreased Proteus mirabilis bacteria.

Proteus mirabilis is a normal member of the human colonic microbial flora that is correlated to rheumatoid arthritis etiology. In this study the blood antibodies (immune complexes) to this microbe were found to decrease following the hypoallergenic diet suggesting a correlation with the stool population of this microbe and arthritic autoimmune reaction.

Cellular Health, Lymphatic System, And Food Sensitivity

Another beneficial effect of the hypoallergenic diet is its regulating effect on the lymphatic system and the extracellular fluid. The lymphatic system acts as a secondary circulatory system. Lymph originates as blood fluid lost from the circulatory system. This fluid, which baths all body tissues, is the medium through which the cells receive dissolved nutrients from the blood. The lymphatic system collects this fluid and returns it to the circulatory system. The portion of the lymph that bathes all cells and tissues is known as the extracellular fluid. The lymphatic system in association with the extracellular fluid functions in delivering the dissolved nutrients to the cells and removing metabolic waste away from the cells.

The lymph and the extracellular fluid also act as a reservoir for positively and negatively charged molecules, respectively known as anions and cations. These charged molecules are necessary for balancing electromagnetic charges on the outside and the inside of the cell. Maintaining a balanced charge is absolutely necessary for proper cell functioning and energy production otherwise known as cellular metabolism.

The connection between partially digested proteins in circulation, the extracellular fluid, and cellular metabolism becomes clear when we consider that proteins, in general, are negatively charged. The presence of these negatively charged proteins in the circulation and in the extracellular fluid disturbs the balanced cellular charges.

In order to re-balance the negative charge of proteins in the extracellular fluid, the cells will release Sodium (Na), which is a positively charged cation molecule, into the extracellular fluid. The movement of sodium is followed by water leaking into the extracellular fluid. Therefore as the undigested protein accumulate in the extracellular fluid, and Sodium (Na) is pumped out of the cells, water will begin to accumulate in the extracellular space. This will increases the total volume of extracellular fluid.

The increase in the extracellular volume will place an excess demand on the lymphatic system. The increase in extracellular fluid will also slow the nutrient delivery since chemicals need to travel a greater distance before they get to the cells. Waste removal will also slow down. Subsequently the health of the cells is compromised and overall cellular metabolism decreases. Decreased cellular metabolism means that a 1000 calories piece of cake, once ingested, for example, will have the equivalent effect of 2000 calories on the body. This decreased cellular metabolism will cause a decreased feeling of overall energy that coincides with weight gain.

Eliminating allergenic and sensitivity causing foods form the diet will decrease the concentration of undigested protein in extracellular fluid and lymph. Due to this cleansing effects on the lymphatic and the extracellular fluid, the diet will optimized cellular metabolism and enhance cellular health and integrity.

Fatigue, Adrenal Gland, And Food Allergies

Another manifestation of food sensitivities can be chronic fatigue. In the previous section, we saw how food allergies contribute to a decreased cellular metabolism and an overall feeling of low energy.

Another major mechanism by which food sensitivities cause low energy and fatigue is by placing an added demand on the adrenal gland leading to Adrenal Fatigue. Adrenal Fatigue is the state of hypo-functioning (decreased functioning) adrenal glands that is not detectable by lab tests

The adrenal glands are small almond shaped glands that sit directly above the kidneys. The role of adrenal glands is to produce cortisol, along with a number of other important hormones.

Cortisol secretion is tightly regulated via the action of sympathetic nervous system. Cortisol serves as stress coping hormone and provides the body with the signal needed for basic daily stress responses. Its amount follows a circadian (daily) rhythm; it surges early in the morning and late afternoon, providing a boost in energy. Cortisol is also the body's natural hormone for dealing with the allergens. Cortisol counteracts the inflammatory and auto-immune effects of allergens in the circulation and the extracellular fluid.

Many prescription drugs for eczema, hives, asthma and other autoimmune diseases use synthetic molecules that are similar to cortisol (Corticosteroid analogs). These prescription drugs do exactly what natural cortisol is supposed to do in the body. Except that they have many side effects.

Chronic stimulation of the sympathetic nervous system (stress response), as well as constant exposure to allergenic foods, will result in constant cortisol secretion from the adrenal gland. The problem with high cortisol is its effect on blood sugar (glucose) and fat synthesis.

Cortisol serves as a signal to the liver to produce and secrete glucose into the blood circulation to meet with the demand of the stress responses. Glucose provides the energy demanded by the fight and flight activity of the sympathetic nervous system.

Following the surges in blood glucose, cells remove the glucose from the circulation to use as energy. This removal is tied in to a period of low blood glucose. Low blood glucose will in turn results in cravings for sugar and other stimulants. The individual with high cortisol secretion will have to eat more of carbohydrate rich foods (high sugar content) and other stimulants, such as coffee, to balance the blood sugar and to simply get through the day.

Cortisol also has a paradoxical effect on the fat cells, especially those around the waste line. It causes these cells to pull glucose out of the circulation and transform it into fat molecules. Cyclical periods of high blood glucose and high cortisol secretion followed by low blood glucose and carbohydrate cravings will therefore results in fat being deposited around the waistline and excess weight gain.

Ultimately this constant secretion of cortisol, due to chronic stress, and food allergies, will affect the adrenal glands' capacity to deal with the high demand. The weakened adrenal gland can no longer cope with the appropriate circadian rhythms of cortisol that are needed to cope with the ordinary stressors of life, and Adrenal Fatigue ensues.

Adrenal Fatigue is associated with a decreased alertness and a pronounced feeling of lethargy that amounts to an inability to muster up the energy to perform basic life functions.

By removing the allergen load, the hypoallergenic diet helps with the rejuvenation of the adrenal glands. Decreased cortisol secretions also regulate blood sugar levels and help with weight loss.

Part Two
How To Do The Hypoallergenic Diet

How To Do The Hypoallergenic Diet

Hypoallergenic Diet is approximately a six to twelve week program. The exact duration depends on the nature of symptoms: the more severe the symptoms the longer the diet. For some conditions it may take longer, so it is important that you plan ahead. The diet is basically divided into two phases: the food elimination phase, and the food challenge phase.

PHASE 1: Food Elimination Phase

The elimination Phase usually takes three weeks. For some individuals with extensive gastrointestinal symptoms and long lasting history of chronic symptoms it may be necessary to continue on this phase for an extra three weeks (total of six weeks) before the GI system gets a chance to heal and the allergens are cleared from the body.[2]

During this Phase you will follow a diet devoid of most food groups that have been shown to cause allergy or sensitivity. These are foods that in general are harder to digest and/or have a high allergenic potential and halt the healing of the gut.

It is very common for individuals to experience a slight aggravation of certain symptoms within the first week of the elimination phase. In general aggravations tend to be mild and fall within such categories as slight diarrhea or constipation, bad breath, hunger, or headaches and common-cold like symptoms. This is generally considered a good sign, and means the body is actively eliminating the toxins and removing the allergens and undigested food proteins. If the initial aggravation lasts longer than a week or the symptoms are unbearable you are advised to contact your doctor.

By the end of the elimination phase the GI mucosa has had sufficient time to heal and the allergens are eliminated from the body. By then, if not sooner in the program, you should notice a marked decrease in your symptoms. If your symptoms have changed slightly but the relief is not substantial it is advised to continue the elimination phase for an extra week or two, before moving onto the food challenge phase.

---

[2] Depending on the nature of symptoms, medical history, and extent of damage to gastrointestinal mucosa, it may be necessary to utilize other naturopathic therapies and supplements, or to extend duration of elimination phase beyond six weeks before gastrointestinal healing is achieved.

How To Prepare Before The Elimination Phase

If your doctor has put you on a hypoallergenic diet, it is because your normal diet has many offending foods. Since that is the case, your cupboards, the fridge, and the restaurants or fast food places you frequent, are filled with these offending foods.

The best way to prepare for the hypoallergenic diet is to *plan ahead*. Set a date. Get the rest of the family involved. Meanwhile, finish all the leftovers and perishable items in the fridge, and store other restricted items out of reach. If it is not possible to take food to work every day, check out the neighborhood at your workplace, and look for places that offer vegan or vegetarian foods or ask the staffs in the restaurants about the ingredients on the menu.

The next thing to do is to *stock up* on allowed foods, including fresh fruits, vegetables, nuts, grains, legumes, oils and condiments. Although organically grown foods that are grown without chemical sprays or insecticides are preferable, they are often more expensive, and are not easily accessible. Fresh produce from your local supermarket will usually suffice. It is also advisable to locate a health food store nearby so that you can purchase the items that are not available at your local supermarket. Keep in mind; prices may vary considerably depending on the health food store; so shop around.

And finally *invest in a juicer*. Most households have a blender/food processor. A juicer however, is the next best investment. A decent quality juicer can nowadays be purchased for less than two hundred dollars. Think of it as an investment. Juicing is a great way to get a nutrient-packed beverage, which is hypoallergenic.

Five Easy Ways To Enhance Gastrointestinal Healing

1-BREATH, TAKE DEEP RELAXED BREATHS

Throughout the day, make sure to take deep relaxed breaths. Breathing is a key to health and healing. It is your direct line of communication with your nervous system. The parasympathetic nervous system responds favorably to increased oxygen levels. By taking regular deep breaths, you can increase the oxygen levels in the body. By breathing deep relaxed breaths you place the body into the healing mode.

So make a breathing anchor. Every time you answer your cell phone, for example, or check the computer, or your watch, remind yourself to check your breathing. And take deep relaxed breaths. This simple but effective method of activating your body's natural healing force is the most powerful medicine you will ever come across.

You can also get small colored paper stickers (light purple or blue is preferred). Stick them in different locations to remind yourself to check your breathing. Every time you see one of these colored stickers take a few of deep relaxed breaths.

2- DRINK WATER

Make sure you are drinking enough water. Water is necessary for cleansing the body. During the first week of the hypoallergenic diet, you may need more water than you are used to. During the hypoallergenic diet the body begins a gentle detoxification process. In order to match the body's needed demands for detoxification proper water intake is crucial. It is necessary to drink at least 6-8 glasses of water per day, in addition to fresh vegetable juices and caffeine free teas.

You can use filtered water or spring water to drink all throughout the day.

Start the day with one cup of room temperature water, with the juice of 1/4 of a fresh lemon added. Drink one cup of water about 1/2 hr. before each meal. But do not drink liquids with foods, as this will dilute the stomach acid and hinder the digestive process. Wait at least 1/2 hr. after your meals before drinking.

3- SMELL YOUR FOOD AND CHEW SUFFICIENTLY

Digestion begins in the mouth through the act of mastication (chewing). The more you chew your food, the less churning your stomach needs to do and the less mechanical sheering it needs to endure. Also by chewing your food to a fine paste, you create a large surface area for the stomach acid to work on. The saliva also has an enzyme for breaking down the soluble starch in foods.

Mastication serves as a signal for the secretion of digestive enzymes and stomach acids. (Hence avoid chewing gum if you have an ulcer, or acid regurgitation). So be sure to chew your meals properly at all the times.

Smelling your food will also activate the secretion of digestive enzymes.

4-MAKE TIME TO ENJOY YOUR FOOD

Once the food is in your GI system, the body will dilate the blood supply of the GI tract, sending more blood to your digestive system. This is necessary for the absorption of essential nutrients. In order for this to happen you need to be in a relaxed parasympathetic mode. Remember that stress and eating on-the-go shuts down the parasympathetic nervous system. So create a safe and quite environment to eat, where you can dedicate enough time to eat, without distractions that would shunt the blood to other areas of your body.

This means no eating on-the-go.

5- EXCERSISE AND WALK

Daily physical activity is part of a healthy life style. Physical activity ensures proper blood and lymphatic circulation. If you are not exercising on regular basis get into the routine of a walking for half an hour to one hour every day.

When possible, go for a short walk about 45 minuets after eating. Ten minutes will be sufficient. The Illio-psoas muscles are active when walking. These twin muscles connect the femur (the bone in your thigh) to the spinal column. That means these muscles pass directly along the digestive organs. Walking therefore, serves as a mechanical facilitator of digestion by moving the food through the GI tract and helping the churning motions of the intestines.

Food Elimination Charts

These charts are designed to eliminate the majority of commonly known food allergens. When following these guidelines, your symptoms should improve significantly. If there are no changes by the end of the sixth week of elimination phase, then chances are, *there may still be some foods that you are sensitive to that have not been eliminated.* It could also be that the cause of your symptoms is not a food sensitivity. In either case, you should *consult with your Doctor,* and make the necessary restrictions to the diet and/or to follow a different approach to the management of your symptoms.

Your doctor may also recommend further restriction to reflect your specific symptoms and medical history. As an example if there is a history of allergy to nuts in your family you may be advised to exclude all nuts from the diet during the elimination phase. Another example would be eliminating all grains except brown rice to enhance the detoxification potential of the diet.

Below is a list of foods you can consume, and the ones to avoid during the Elimination Phase. (You will find a replica of these charts at the end of the book to detach or photocopy)

Vegetables:	
Consume	❑ All fresh vegetables (try to incorporate all vegetables such as asparagus, brussel sprouts, celery, cauliflower, cabbage onions, garlic, carrots, beets, leeks, green beans, broccoli, leafy greens: spinach, kale, mustard greens, turnip greens, bok choy, watercress, etc.) ❑ Sweet potatoes, Yams, Squash, Pumpkin, (Very soothing on the GI) ❑ Sprouts: sunflower sprouts, pea and bean sprouts (esp. alfalfa & red clover as they help with detoxification)
Avoid	❑ Tomatoes, corn, mushrooms, green peppers, red pepper, bell peppers, potatoes ❑ If ragweed allergy present then eliminate artichokes, iceberg lettuce, sunflower seeds, dandelion, chamomile and chicory.

Juicing breaks the vegetable cells and releases a rich source of enzymes making digestion easier. For the purpose of Hypoallergenic Diet avoid raw vegetables as they are difficult to digest. The exceptions to this rule are fresh squeezed vegetable juices, sprouts, and tender vegetables such as lettuce, leafy herbs, and peeled cucumbers.

Otherwise consume your vegetables steamed, baked, or stir-fried in water and olive oil, or Coconut oil.

Fruits:	
Consume	❑ All fresh/frozen fruits (see exceptions below) ❑ All berries fresh or frozen (except strawberries) ❑ All jams and fruit sauces of allowed fruits (with no sugars or preservatives added)
Avoid	❑ Bananas ❑ Citrus (oranges, grapefruit, and any citric acid containing beverage) ❑ kiwi ❑ Melons ❑ Strawberries ❑ Peaches and apricots ❑ Apples ❑ Dried fruits (does not include dates, organic-sulfite free raisins, dried figs, or unsweetened dried sulfite free cranberries)

Small amounts of fresh lemon/lime juice may be allowed unless strictly forbidden by your doctor, or if you have either esophageal burning, or a gastric ulcer.

Avoid eating fruits up to two hours after meals, as they slow the digestion process. The exception to this rule is cooked fruits and fruit sauces.

Grains and Cereals:	
Consume	❑ Brown rice, rice, buckwheat, quinoa, teff, amaranth ❑ Pasta, cereals and pastry made from these grains.
Avoid	❑ All gluten-containing grains (wheat, spelt, rye, oats, barley) and breads, pasta & other products from flour of these

Brown rice contains phytic acid that helps with detoxifying the tissues in the body. This is great for the purpose of the Hypoallergenic Diet (See recipe section for rice). However, if brown rice is going to be used as the main grain in the diet for the long term, then it is best to remove the phytic acid since too much phytic acid can remove beneficial minerals from the body. Soaking the brown rice in water over night can help remove the phytic acid content.

Legumes and Lentils:	
Consume	❑ All legumes: beans and lentils (all beans, fresh/frozen/dried, except soy) ❑ All peas (fresh/frozen/dried)
Avoid	❑ Soy beans & soy products (tofu, soy milk, soy sauce, miso, tempeh, TVP)

In the preparation of legumes and lentils, use abundant amounts of the following spices: cumin, fennel, mint, or ginger. These herbs and spices help with the digestion of proteins found in legumes, and help prevent symptoms of abdominal bloating and gas that commonly occur after legume consumption. Another option is drinking a tea made from equal parts of ginger (2cm fresh sliced), fennel (1 tsp), and cumin (1 tsp), before or after heavy legume dishes.

If using canned beans, be sure to rinse with cold water several times before using.

Nuts and seeds:	
Consume	❑ Raw almonds, walnuts, ❑ Sesame seeds, pumpkin seeds, sunflower seeds
Avoid	❑ Peanuts, pistachios, cashews, brazil nuts, hazelnuts, pecans ❑ Any nuts or seeds that are salted or flavored in some way

Avoid roasted or salted nuts as the heating can make the oils go rancid. It is best to buy the nuts in shells, as the shells keep them preserved.

Presoaking nuts can help make them tender, and will help removing the skin as well.

Animal products:	
Consume	❑ Free-range chicken & turkey breast (if not free-range then organic or grain fed) ❑ Lamb (best if organic) ❑ Wild game ❑ Wild Fish of any kind (except Shark, Swordfish, King mackerel, and Tilefish) ❑ Farmed organic fish
Avoid	❑ Red meats (beef, pork, bacon), processed meats (hotdogs, salami, wieners, sausage, canned meats, smoked meats) these all contain flower additives and coloring and preservatives ❑ Dairy (milk, cream, sour cream, cheese, butter, yogurt) ❑ Eggs ❑ Sea food: Shell-fish, Shrimp, Lobster, Scallops, Crab ❑ Catfish, Shark, Swordfish, King mackerel, and Tilefish ❑ Farmed Inorganic Fish

Most commercially available turkeys are injected with chemicals and are basted with milk, corn starch and tenderizers, etc. Avoid them and buy only fresh turkey. The label will usually state if a fresh turkey has not been treated.

Oils:	
Consume	❑ Virgin olive oil, cold or with low heat cooking ❑ Coconut oil for high heat cooking ❑ Cold pressed sunflower oil, sesame oil, and flax oil for dressing and no heat recipes
Avoid	❑ All other oils ❑ Refined oils, margarine, shortening

Adding small amounts of water to the oils, when stir-frying, will keep the temperature low and you can avoid creating toxic chemicals that are produced when the oils are overheated.

Condiments:	
Consume	❑ Sea salt ❑ All herbs (e.g. parsley, coriander, watercress, dill, basil, thyme, oregano, garlic, ginger) ❑ Most spices (e.g. turmeric, fennel, cinnamon, black pepper) ❑ Spreads: nut/seed butters (e.g. almond, sesame (tahini), sunflower), bean dips (e.g. hummus) ❑ Sauces: pesto, mustard with no additives ❑ Apple cider ❑ Sweeteners: stevia (whole plant, unprocessed) and un-pasteurized honey in moderation.
Avoid	❑ Regular table salt (table salt is not necessarily a food allergen, it just does not have the added minerals and benefits of sea salt) ❑ Avoid peppers from the nightshade family (cayenne pepper, red pepper, paprika, jalapeno, curry mix (contains red pepper in the mix)) ❑ All sweeteners (corn/ brown rice/ maple syrups, molasses, brown/ white sugar, glucose, maltose, maltodextrose, etc.) This includes desserts & all processed foods high in sugars. ❑ MSG ❑ All food additives, preservatives, and coloring.

Use turmeric, fennel, and other aromatic spices abundantly. Turmeric specifically has many anti-inflammatory qualities and can help reduce allergenic responses.

Drinks:		
Consume	❑	Filtered water or spring water, at least 6-8 glasses/day
	❑	100% fresh fruit & fresh vegetable juices
	❑	Herbal teas: roobois tea, peppermint, nettle leaf tea, chamomile, licorice root, passion flower, dandelion, borage tea, milk thistle, and any other herbal tea.
	❑	Green tea
	❑	Rice milk (unsweetened)
	❑	Almond milk (unsweetened)
Avoid	❑	Caffeinated beverages (coffee, black tea, soda) (green tea is an exception)
	❑	Alcohol
	❑	Dairy (milk & other dairy products)
	❑	Soy milk
	❑	All fruit drinks high in refined sugar and added sugar
	❑	All vegetable drinks high in salt

The following is a list of some foods with less allergenic potential. These may *infrequently* cause allergies and sensitivities and have not been listed on the avoided lists. They are only listed for your information.

The pea family (lentils, garbanzos, alfalfa, and bean sprouts, guar gum, and licorice)
The lily family (asparagus, chives, garlic, leeks, onions)
Sunflower family (artichoke, lettuce, sunflower)
Parsley family (Celery, carrots, parsnip, anise, caraway)
Laurel family (avocado, bay leaf, camphor, cinnamon, sassafras)
Nuts (including walnuts and almonds)

Shopping Tips

Shopping For Fresh Produce

Perishable foods include vegetables, fruits, and herbs. These are foods that you buy on daily or weekly basis, and depend on the recipe you are planning to make. The issue with perishable foods is the source and manner of cultivation or farming. As a general rule of thumb it is preferred to purchase these foods as locally grown and organic.

Organic farming is intended to reduce the impact of agriculture on our environment. By eating organic foods, you limit your exposure to synthetic insecticides, fungicides and herbicides, artificial dies, sulfite, and other preservatives, because these chemicals are not applied to organic crops, you also help with the sustainability of agricultural land.

Also there is growing evidence that organic foods have higher nutrient content. A study in the Journal of the American College of Nutrition in 2004, entitled Changes in USDA Food Composition Data for 43 Garden Crops, 1950 to 1999, compared vegetables analyzed in 1950 and in 1999, and found noticeable decreases in conventionally grown crops in six of 13 nutrients examined (the six were: protein, calcium, phosphorus, iron, riboflavin and ascorbic acid). Reductions in calcium, phosphorus, iron and ascorbic acid were also found relative to organically grown crops.

If costs and availability of organic produce is an issue for you, you are not alone. On average organic foods costs more per item, and are subject to seasonal availability. What you want to know is that there are 12 produce that consistently show a high level of contamination. So it is advisable to obtain these as organic:

These foods are: spinach, bell peppers, nectarines, pears, strawberries, peaches, cherries, raspberries, celery, grapes, potatoes, and apples.
On the other hand the 12 least contaminated produce items are: asparagus, avocados, bananas, broccoli, cauliflower, kiwi fruits, mangos, onions, papaya, pineapples, peas (sweet), and corn.

Shopping For Meat

For the most part, old animal farming practices have been replaced by large confinement facilities that produce a year-round supply of meat and chickens at a reasonable price. Although the food is cheap and convenient, factory farming is creating a host of problems. Animal stress and abuse, air, land, and water pollution, the widespread use of hormones, antibiotics, and other drugs, and food with less nutritional value are among the most problematic.

Factory farming is designed to boost animal productivity and lower costs. This means that the animals are fed on grains rather than free ranching on grass and in pastures. Feeding large amounts of any type of grain to a grazing animal will reduce the nutritional value of the meat because grain has fewer of these nutrients than fresh pasture. For example, compared with grass-fed beef, grain-fed beef has only one quarter as much vitamin E, one-eighth as much beta-carotene, and one-third as many omega-3 fatty acids.

So as far as meats go the best choice of all is buying organic certified grass fed products. However sources are less common and prices are significantly higher than for conventional food.

Your second best choice is therefore grass fed meat. There are two reasons for choosing grass fed meat over organic grain fed meat: first is the superior nutritional content, and second is that most grass-farmers avoid the use of pesticides, herbicides, hormones, and antibiotics even though they are not striving for full organic certification. What keeps most farmers from attaining the official 'organic' designation is that they use nitrogen fertilizers on their fields or treat their animals with medications to rid them of parasites.

For the purpose of Hypoallergenic Diet you are allowed to consume lamb. Sheep are free ranching animals and *can not* be confined. Therefore if organic lamb is not available to you, regular lamb will suffice.

For similar reasons, it is best to obtain free run, organic chicken or turkey. Alternatively you can get free run only. Since free run chicken get to eat a myriad of bugs and other living things they desire, they are nutritionally superior. Avoid factory-farmed chicken as they tend to be high in hormones

Shopping For Fish

The issue with wild fish is environmental contaminations such as mercury and other heavy metals. Mercury is a toxic heavy metal that can accumulate in fish. The body can handle small amount of this heavy metal. Frequent exposure can cause mercury accumulation in the body. Eating fish with high levels of mercury can negatively impact brain development, nervous system, learning and memory function. Certain fish species are known to have higher mercury concentrations than others, sometimes due to polluted waters. In general fish with higher fat content, and large, predatory fish at the top of the food chain, accumulate the most mercury and contaminates.

The most mercury-contaminated fish that should be avoided are shark, swordfish, king mackerel, and tilefish.

The second most contaminated group of fish are albacore (white) tuna, grouper, marlin, orange roughly, bass (sea and largemouth), halibut, red snapper, spanish mackerel, bluefish, lobster, pike, walleye. You should limit your intake of this group to no more that once serving every three weeks.

The less contaminated group, which you can consume up to 2 servings a week are Atlantic mackerel, haddock, salmon, trout, cod, catfish, her-ring, whitefish, mahi mahi, and shad. Also canned light tuna because of its small size and low fat content is low on contamination chart since it is a smaller variety compared to the albacore ("white") tuna, which contains higher levels of mercury.

Other small fish such as sardines, anchovies, and Alaskan pollock would be among the least contaminated sources and you can consume abundantly.

Another common contamination that is of concern with fish, especially in farmed fish, is PCBs (polychlorinated biphenyls). PCBs are industrial pollutants that find their way into fresh waters and oceans where they are absorbed by fish. They are also a major contaminant found in fish food used in the farming industry. Potential health effects of PCBS include impaired memory and learning, and adverse effects on the immune, reproductive, and nervous systems. PCBs are also potential human carcinogens, known to promote cancer in animals.

Farmed fish poses other issues too. Disease is always a problem when fish are raised in close quarters, and aquaculture has adopted use of antibiotics and antiparasitic drugs to remedy the issue. Some of the antibiotics that fish farmers give their stock to minimize disease also pass easily into the surrounding environment, and some are highly toxic to humans and the environment.

For general health reasons as far as farmed fish goes if possible buy organic farmed fish, or purchase wild fish only. You can also reduce PCB exposure from fish by removing the skin and visible fat.

General Shopping Tips

Avoid most canned, packaged, processed, or chemically contaminated foods. For mere reasons of convenience you may use canned beans, especially if you can find brands without preservatives, although it is best to cook your own beans and lentils. It is really simple to cook beans, as long as you remember to presoak them overnight. When making beans, always make some extra, and store them away in tightly sealed jars. Pack the beans into the jar when the beans/lentils are still warm, and leave as little air as possible on the top. This will seal the jar air–tight, and you can store your jars in the fridge for about 2-3 weeks before loosing any quality. This will save you a lot of cooking time.

If you use canned or packaged foods, *read the labels* carefully to be sure that it is a pure food, with nothing added. Avoid anything with added sugar, glucose, fructose, flavoring, color, added starch, or any preservatives. If you are not familiar with any of the listed ingredients on a label the odds are it is not good for you.

Some sardines and other fish are canned in vegetable oil. However, since the oil may be of an unknown source, buy fish packed in water, or in its own oil or in olive oil. Sardines packed in olive oil or sardine oil make a good snack. Tuna and salmon packed in spring water or olive oil is also acceptable.

Stock up on allowed nuts and seeds. These are the most ancient sources of our nutrition and an integral part of traditional diets. They have high amounts of proteins, good fat contents, and a balanced carbohydrate profile. They are also a rich source of compact fiber. Make nuts and seeds a part of your every day diet. It is the single most important step you can take after increasing your vegetable consumption and avoiding processed foods.

When buying nut butter make sure it is non-hydrogenated. In non-hydrogenated nut butters, the nut oil separates, and usually forms a layer of oil on top of the nut butter. Use this as a way to distinguish them from hydrogenated nut butters.

Some of the items in the following shopping list you need to stock on or have 2-3 serving handy so that you won't have to run out to the grocery store every time you want to cook. Before going on a shopping spree, it is best to take time to glance over the recipe section, and find a few recipes that you want to try, and plan ahead that way.

Nuts And Seeds
Almonds (whole unsalted, slivered, or ground)
Walnuts (whole)
Pumpkin seeds
Sesame seeds
Sunflower seeds
(Store these in a sealed container in the freezer to avoid the oils from going rancid)

Oils
Olive oil (for low heat cooking)
Coconut oil (for high heat cooking)
Sesame seed oil (for flavoring)
Flax seed oil (for dressing)

Grains And Legumes (try to get variety in your diet, but remember you're allowed to have favorites)

Brown Rice
Brown Rice Pasta
Long Grain White Rice
Whole Flax Seeds
Buckwheat
Quinoa
Buckwheat and Quinoa flour
Arrowroot flour (as a thickener in recipes)
Chickpea flour
Beans and Lentils (bulk red and green lentils, split peas, kidney beans, chickpeas, mung beans, etc.)
Split peas; green, red, and yellow

Condiments and Other
Dried herbs (basil, thyme, oregano, marjoram, mint)
Honey (un-pasteurized)
Teas (green tea, herbal teas)
Raisins (organic or sulfite free)

Sauces
Coconut milk
Pomegranate reduction (from Mediterranean stores) or Pomegranate juice
Dijon mustard (organic or sulfite free)
Apple cider vinegar
Balsamic vinegar (sulfite free)
Tahini

Frozen food
Frozen Fish
Frozen berries
Frozen peas

Canned Food
Tuna (in water or olive oil, no preservatives)
Salmon (in water or olive oil, no preservatives)
Canned beans (with no additives or preservatives)

Phase 2: Food Challenge Phase

After the Elimination Phase is complete, it is time to identify which of the eliminated foods were the causes of allergy or sensitivity. The method of reintroducing the eliminated foods back into the diet, one at a time, is called Food Challenge.

Food Challenge is done by reintroducing a food item back on the diet, one item at a time, and for three consecutive days each time. Here you will consume the challenge food item for at least two out of three daily meals for two consecutive days. During these two days, you should monitor for any symptoms and continue this monitoring process for an extra third day. On this third day, you are to consume only foods allowed on Food Elimination Charts and avoid the challenge food.

For example, if you were to challenge tomatoes into your diet, then you will eat tomatoes in any two of the following meals: breakfast, lunch, or dinner for two consecutive days. Then revert back to the Elimination Phase on the third day, without any tomatoes. If any of your symptoms resurface during any of these three days, then you know you are sensitive or allergic to tomatoes. The next step is to go back onto the Elimination Phase until your symptoms disappear before you move on to challenge the next food item.

When you notice symptoms within the first day of a challenging a food item then there is no need to keep eating that food on the second day. Then you must go back on the Elimination Phase until your symptoms subside before challenging the next food. You must also avoid that sensitivity causing food in your diet.

The most important thing in the Food Challenge Phase is monitoring your health for any old symptoms that may return or any new ones that may come up. It is important to continue to monitor for sensitivity reactions on the third day because many food allergy reactions do not show up right away, and may have delayed reactions a few days later. Sensitivities may manifest as: nausea, bloating, gas, constipation, upset stomach, itching, sneezing, headaches, runny nose, restless sleep, fatigue, or worsening of previous symptoms.

If you do not notice any changes in your health by the end of the third day of a food challenge, then it is safe to assume that you are not sensitive to that food. You can keep that food in your diet and move on to the next food item.

In the case of tomatoes, for example, if tomatoes did not elicit any symptoms by the third day, then you can conclude that you are not sensitive to tomatoes, and can include it in your diet from then on. But do this in moderation, while challenging the next food.

Keeping the potential allergenic foods in moderation is important, since food allergies can have a cumulative effect. Even if you are not reacting strongly to a particular food, it may contribute to sensitivity reactions when combined with other allergenic foods. Therefore, it is important to consume potential allergen/sensitivity foods in moderation in order to properly test for reactions from other foods.

Below is the list of food groups that need to be reintroduced into your diet. The order of food reintroduction can be altered according to your situation, and the advice of your Naturopathic or Medical Doctor. (You will find a copy of this List in the back of the book to detach or photocopy)

1-Dairy (milk, cream, sour cream, cheese, butter, yogurt).
For this food group, it is advisable to introduce one item at a time, rather than the whole group of dairy foods, since you may be able to tolerate some items, but not all of them. For example, many people can tolerate certain varieties of cheese, but can have sensitivity to milk.

2-All gluten-containing grains (wheat, spelt, rye, oats, barley).
Commonly found in breads, pastas, & other products from refined flour. It is advisable to test oats separately, since oats may be better tolerated than the others.

3-Soy beans & soy products (tofu, soy milk, soy sauce, miso, tempeh, TVP).
Even if you find no sensitivity to soy products, make sure you moderate them in your diet as excess consumption can cause sensitivity over time.

4-Unprocesssed animal meats: beef and pork.

5-Corn Products

6-Processed meats.

Keep in mind, processed meats such as salami, ham, etc., generally have modified milk ingredients, corn starch, wheat, and preservatives.

6- Eggs

7-Nightshade family of plants : bell Peppers, tomatoes, potatoes, and eggplant.
These are better when reintroduced separately since the extent of sensitivity to one does not equal in sensitivity to other members of the family.

8- Citrus (oranges, grapefruit)

9- Mushrooms

10- Sea food, Shellfish, Catfish.

18-All sweeteners (corn/ brown rice/ maple syrups, molasses, brown/ white sugar, etc.)
All fruit drinks are high in refined sugars

11- Caffeinated beverages (coffee, black tea, soda)

12- Peanuts, pistachios, cashews, hazelnuts (one item at a time)

13-Strawberries

14-Bananas

13-Apples

16-Melons

17-Dried fruits

18-All other eliminated foods, one item at a time

By the end of the food reintroduction phase, you will have identified the different foods you are allergic or sensitive to. The identification of these foods will help you with the food choices that keep your body and mind healthy. Of course not all rules are written in stone, and you may choose to indulge in these foods on occasions, at a party for example. But you will know what to expect the next day, and be better prepared to deal with it.

A noteworthy observation is that the longer you avoid the foods which caused sensitivity (not allergy), the less intense your symptoms are going to be when you eat them on a later date. You may even be able to consume them later without any problems. So don't be discouraged if you find that you are sensitive to a food group. Try it later, or in different recipes, and see if your body can tolerate it. Find out about the traditional methods of preparation for that food group and use those methods in your cooking.

In essence, there are no ideal foods, only ideal portions and ideal modes of preparation. Beyond these ideal portions and depending on an individual's genetic make-up, the body may be burdened and unable to tolerate these foods.

The next step after completing the Hypoallergenic Diet is to know the amounts, portions, and the frequency of foods that you can consume before getting any of your old symptoms back. This will come naturally since, your awareness of the intimate connection between food and your general health will have increased. This state of heightened awareness of your optimal health and body function can also help you with your day-to-day choices of food. **Keep in mind that we all have the intuitive knowledge to choose the diet that suits our body best. It is the habitual consumption of packaged and processed foods that masks this ability.**

PART 3
The Rationale Behind The Elimination
Of Some Main Food Groups

Milk And Dairy Products

Milk is composed of water, protein, lactose, minerals, fats, and a variety of other substances. There are over 30 different proteins in milk, and these are broadly categorized as members of the casein or whey proteins. Full fat certified raw milk and milk products, when consumed in moderation, are an excellent source of protein, vitamin B12, and many other nutrients. Pasteurized, homogenized milk, and reduced fat-content milk products, however, are among the top food allergens.

Milk comes packed with all the enzymes necessary for its digestion. The process of heating and homogenization denatures (destroys) many of the enzymes and proteins in the milk. Without these enzymes, milk proteins cannot be completely digested, and milk looses much of its nutrient potential. Consider that a newly born calf depends on these intrinsic enzymes, and cannot survive on the milk of its mother if it is pasteurized.

Aside from the decreased nutritional value, the undigested proteins in pasteurized milk (mainly a protein family known as casein) can cross through the blood stream and bind to different neurons in the brain causing changes in mood and behavior.

In addition, homogenization of the milk transforms the healthy butterfat into microscopic spheres. These spheres are small enough that they pass through the stomach and small intestine wall without first being digested. These microscopic fats spheres contain an enzyme known as xanthine oxidase (XO). XO is a powerful digestive enzyme. Once in the circulation, XO breaks free from its fat sphere and attacks the inner wall of arteries. This can result in inflammation, and other immune responses.

Substitutions to milk:

Milk allergy and lactose intolerance are generally discussed in relation to cow's milk. There are other forms of milk and dairy in the market that are less allergenic. They are mainly goat's milk and sheep's milk. Although it is best to avoid these sources during the hypoallergenic diet, you can try these alternative sources once the diet is complete, to see how you respond to them.

The best alternative to milk is unsweetened almond milk and rice milk. The Following are two home recipes.

Almond Milk

Ingredients

1 cup	raw almonds
4 cup	boiled water
1 tbsp	un-pasteurized honey
1/4 tsp	sea salt
1/2 cup	water

Method

Soak nuts in water and salt over night.
Place in a blender, and add honey. Blend thoroughly and strain. Place the almond pulp back in the blender, add 1/2 cup water, blend again, and strain. Keep refrigerated.

Generally keeps for 3-5 days.

Rice milk

Ingredients

2 cups	cooked brown rice or other rice
5-6 cups	boiled water
2 tbsp	sesame oil
1 tbsp	un-pasteurized honey
1/4 tsp	sea salt
1/2 cup	water

Method

Soak cooked rice over night in water and salt. Place in a blender with other ingredients. Blend thoroughly and strain. Place the rice pulp back in the blender, add 1/2 cup water, blend again, and strain. Refrigerate.

Generally keeps 1 week in the fridge.

Wheat And Wheat Products, And Other Gluten Containing Grains.

Wheat contains a number of proteins, including albumin, globulin, gliadin and glutenin. The majority of allergies to wheat involve the albumin and globulin fractions, but gluten may also cause allergic reactions.

Gluten is composed of two protein groups, namely gliadins and glutenins, which provide the flow quality and elasticity to the finished wheat products. Gliadin is a type of prolamin (a group of proteins with similar protein structures). Other grains, such as rye and barley, contain their own prolamins. By definition, gluten is found only in wheat, although the term is commonly used to refer to any similar prolamin protein.

Corn is another grain that is avoided in the hypoallergenic diet. Although corn is said to be "gluten free," experience indicates that grain-allergic patients often do not usually tolerate it well. Avoiding corn involves the corn-derived sugars, including dextrose (also known as glucose or corn sugar), dextrin, dextrates, and maltodextrin. It also involves caramel or malt syrup, and distilled white vinegar, because they may also be sources of corn-derived products.

Oats is another one of the grains that is best kept away during the diet. Although there is controversy around this issue, since consumption of oats seems to be safe for people with food sensitivity. In fact oat has an excellent healing influence on the mucus membrane. However, it should be considered that most commercial oat products contain wheat, flour, or gluten. Contamination of oats with wheat may occur due to the sharing of equipment in grain processing and the rotation of crops (wheat may be grown on the same fields as oats were). Therefore, contamination may be the cause of adverse reactions to oats often reported by gluten-sensitive individuals.

Substitutions for wheat and other grains:

Rice

Rice is an ancient food, and arguably the most important grain grown in the world. It has been intimately involved in the culture as well as the economy of many societies.

Of all the grains, long grain brown rice is least likely to cause problems. All other grains of rice can also be consumed safely, but don't have the nutritional value of that found in brown rice. Of all the available grains, sticky rice is most likely to cause any sensitivity as the adhesion of the grains may decrease chances of proper digestion by keeping the digestive enzymes away.

The protein profile of rice is not complete; it lacks an essential amino acid called lysine. The body cannot make lysine and has to get it from other food sources. Therefore it is recommended to use almonds and other nuts and seeds in recipes that involve rice. You can also consume rice along side protein sources, such as legumes or hypoallergenic meats.

Brown rice is a rich source of phytic acid. The supplemental version of this chemical is called IP6, and is a part of a total approach to detoxifying the body during cancer therapy. Having brown rice during the hypoallergenic diet, therefore, will help with a gentle detoxification of body tissues.

Although beneficial in cleaning the body when used in moderation, too much phytic acid can leach good minerals out of the tissues. Therefore, if brown rice is the main grain in your diet and you consume it more that 3-4 times a week, it is recommended to soak the rice in water overnight, as it will release the phytic acid. Alternatively, you can boil the rice in abundant amounts of water for 5 min, and dispose the water before cooking. This however, may not be necessary during the hypoallergenic diet, as a gentle detoxification is desirable.

Quinoa

Quinoa is not really a grain, nor is it a cereal. It is the seed of a leafy plant from the goosefoot family that is distantly related to spinach and beets. This is the crop that sustained the ancient Incas. Nutritionally, quinoa is a supergrain. It has excellent reserves of protein, and unlike grains, is not missing the amino acid lysine. So the protein is more complete (a trait it shares with other "non-true" grains such as buckwheat and amaranth).

Buckwheat

Buckwheat is not wheat at all. It is the seed of a leafy plant. Originally cultivated in the cooler countries of Central Asia, buckwheat arrived in North America in the 1600s.

When cooked, buckwheat seeds tend to have a sticky nature and buckwheat flour makes a great substitution in pastry and bread.

This seed has a balanced amino acid profile, a good source of B vitamins, and is rich in phosphorus, potassium, iron, and calcium.

Teff

Teff is an ancient cereal that belongs to the lovegrass family of plants and has originated in Ethiopia. Teff seeds are small (less than 1 mm diameter). Because of the minute size of teff, the bulk of the grain consists of bran and germ. This makes teff nutrient dense, as the bran and germ are the most nutritious parts of any grain. This grain has very high calcium content, and contains high levels of phosphorous, iron, copper, aluminum, barium, and thiamin. It also has a good protein profile that includes lysine.

Amaranth

Amaranth is a tall plant with very broad leaves. It is closely related to spinach. The seeds are tiny, lens shaped, and are a golden to cream tan color.

Amaranth is a versatile grain that can be cooked as a cereal, ground into flour, popped like popcorn, sprouted, or toasted. The flour has a pasty quality relative to teff, or quinoa flower and can be used in preparation of flatbreads, pancakes and pastas.

As a rule of thumb it is best not to mix different grains in the same recipe. Since this will increase the protein variation and can hinder proper digestion.

Egg

The allergenic potential with eggs is simply due to the large number of the proteins that are present in it.

Substitution for eggs:
In pastry recipes that call for eggs, the best substitute for each egg is 1 table spoon of fresh ground flax seed in 1/3 cup of boiling water.

Animal meat

Similar to the eggs, beef and pork also have a large number of proteins in them. The same is true for other sources of animal proteins, except that beef (and pork) are two of the most indigestible forms of animal proteins.

Sugar

Sugar is not an allergen per say, but is a potent inducer of inflammatory processes in the body. Sugar activates mast cells (a group of cells in the mucosa) to release histamine. Histamine causes inflammation, and inflammation is the mechanism by which allergen-induced immune reactions are sustained. The runny nose and stuffiness that many people experience during allergy season is due to the action of histamine. Therefore an effective Hypoallergenic Diet is not possible without the elimination of refined sugars from the diet also.

Substitutions for sugar:
Un-pasteurized and unheated honey is allowed in moderation.

Using dates and raisins in recipes, and using them with teas, is another way of satisfying any cravings for sweets. Keep in mind that these substitutes have high sugar contents, and if used too frequently, will have the same effect of the refined sugar.

Stevia (also called sweetleaf) is another great substitution for sugar. Stevia belongs to the sunflower family and is native to subtropical and tropical South America and Central America. The plant has been used for centuries by the Native Americans of Paraguay and Brazil as a sweetener in Yerba Mate and medicinal teas.

When using stevia, in his book Healing With Whole Foods, Paul Pitchford cautions, "Obtain only the green or brown [whole] stevia extracts or powders; avoid the clear extracts and white powders, which, highly refined and lacking essential phyto-nutrients, cause imbalance".

Coffee, Caffeinated Products, And Chocolate

Caffeine is the most frequently used stimulant in the world. Coffee, tea, aspirin, diet pills, many soft drinks, and even some herbal preparations contain caffeine or very closely related substances known as alkaloids. Chocolate, and cocoa for example have a closely related alkaloid known as theobromine.

In general caffeine and theobromine are not allergenic. The problem with these chemicals is that they are very acidic and irritate the mucosa in the small intestine. The acidity of these chemical eats away at the villi, reducing the effectiveness of digestion and making the damaged mucosa prone to allowing undigested proteins pass through and enter the blood circulation.

The acidity of the caffeine also taxes the body's buffering reserves, oftentimes to the detriments of bone health. The extra acidity of the body in habitual coffee and soft drink consumers, is balanced by calcium and other minerals that are pulled out of the bone, thus reducing the strength and density of bone as a result.

Coffee is also a potent stimulator of sympathetic nervous system and the adrenal glands. Frequent consumption exhausts the adrenal glands causing further exhaustion of bodies own ability to deal with allergens.

The other problem with coffee is the plantations. Aside from the moral and economical issue of the plantations where large profits stay in the hand of the corporate land owners, coffee plantations rely heavily on use of herbicides and pesticides. These chemicals are dangerous to the body.

It is of course possible to obtain de-acidified, organic, fair trade coffee. But for the purpose of the hypoallergenic diet, coffee, chocolate, cocoa, and black tea need to be eliminated from the diet, in order for the GI to have sufficient time to heal.

Substitutions for coffee, black tea and chocolate:

A good replacement source of caffeine is *green tea*. Green tea in not nearly as acidic as coffee, and it has a wide range of antioxidants that have been proven to be beneficial to the body. It also does not irritate the GI mucosa. Most Naturopathic Doctors agree that the antioxidant benefits of the green tea, by far, outweigh any potential harm from its caffeine content. Green tea should be considered as the beverage of choice for those who are heavy coffee consumers, as it will lessen the withdrawal symptoms (mainly headaches) associated with removing coffee from the diet.

Roobois tea is another good replacement with high antioxidant content for black tea drinkers. It does not contain caffeine.

Another herbal tea that is rich in calcium and minerals that also helps with the healing of a damaged small intestine, is *nettle leaf tea.*

You can also use 100% pure *carob powder* as a substitute for chocolate. (Make sure it does not contain sugar or starch.)

Hot Carob drink

(1 serving)

Ingredients

4 tsp	carob powder
1.5 cup	water
1/3 tsp	cinnamon powder
Dash	nutmeg
To taste	un-pasteurized honey
To taste	almond milk

Method

Bring water to a boil. Add ingredients and stir on low heat for 4-5 minutes. Place in a cup and add honey and almond milk to taste.

Green Tea Chai

(2 servings)

Ingredients
1	medium cinnamon stick
3	star anise seeds
1tsp	cardamom buds
1/2 tsp	clove buds
1/2tsp	black pepper pods
1 cm	fresh ginger root (optional)
2tsp	green tea loose leaves (2 tea bag)
To taste	almond/rice milk (if desired)

Method
Place herb and spice ingredients (except green tea) in a saucepan, with 4 cups of water. Bring to a boil, cover and simmer on low heat for 15 minutes. Remove the pan from the heat and strain into 2 cups. Place green tea (loose leaves in a tea strainer, or the tea bags) in the cups and allow to simmer for 2-5 minutes.
Add almond milk and honey as desired.

The spice and seed combination can be reused up to 3 times, as long as it is within the same week. So store the seeds and spices in the fridge.

Variation
You can use the spice decoction with any other tea. Roobois tea is a great alternative to green tea in this recipe.

Alcohol and alcoholic drink

Much like the alkaloids in the coffee, alcohol has toxic effect on the mucosal lining of the gastrointestinal tract. Alcohol irritates the mucosal cells, leading to damage and inflammation, and even ulceration in long term use.

Substitution:

Mulled Wine Beverage (de-alcoholized)

(4 serving)

Ingredients

750 ml	bottle of full bodied red wine, (organic, low sulfite)
3 cups	water
1	pear, peeled and cut into 8 pieces.
1	medium mango cut in slices
1tsp	cloves
1/2 tsp	green cardamom buds
3	medium cinnamon stick (2 tsp ground)
1/4 tsp	nutmeg
1/3 cup	un-pasteurized honey

Method

Pour the red wine into saucepan and heat it gradually. Keep it heated for 30 minutes until most of the alcohol evaporates. Add the rest of ingredients and bring to a boil, boil on med to low heat for 15-20 minutes. Pour into glasses/mugs through a strainer.

Alternatively you can drink the beverage chilled.

Part 4
Recipes

Recipes with (*) mark are the author's favorites

Breakfast

Breakfast is the most important meal of the day. Generally we tend to have three or four breakfast ideas that we rotate through. A balanced breakfast will provide you with the nutrients necessary to keep you going throughout the day.

(Unless stated the breakfast recipes are 1 serving)

Brown Rice Porridge

Ingredients

1 cup	precooked brown rice
1 cup	rice milk
1 cup	water
3	pitted fresh dates, cut into pieces
2 tbsp	sliced raw almonds/ almond butter
dash	ground cinnamon

Method

Place ingredients in a saucepan and bring to boil.
Stir for 4-5 minuets while boiling.
Boil off to the desired consistency.
Serve in a bowl sprinkled with cinnamon.

Alternatively, for a creamy texture, using a blender, you can puree the rice with the water and the rice milk before placing the ingredients in the sauce pan.

Variations

Dates can be replaced with a handful of raisins, or 1/2 cup frozen or fresh mixed berries. Un-pasteurized honey can be added to achieve desired sweetness.

Dash of cinnamon can be replaced by turmeric powder (turmeric needs to be added to the pot before serving).

Sweet Pear Porridge

(Serves 2)

Ingredients

1/2 cup	quinoa
2 cups	water
1/2 cup	coconut milk
1	fresh pear, seeded, cut in small chunks
1 tsp	arrowroot flour
2 tbsp	pumpkin seeds
1 tsp	un-pasteurized honey (optional)

Method

Place quinoa in a saucepan and roast for 1-2 min (stirring continuously).
Add 2 cups of water and the pears. Bring to a boil and boil for 8-10 min.
Mix in the arrow root flour into the coconut milk and add to the sauce pan.
Boil for another 10 minuets. Remove from heat. Serve in a bowl topped with pumpkin seeds. Sweeten with honey to desired sweetness.

Variations

Pears can be replaced by cooked rhubarb or fresh mangoes.

Buckwheat Porridge

Ingredients

3 tbsp	buckwheat flour
1 cup	water
1/2 cup	rice milk or almond milk
2 tbsp	tahini or ground walnuts or almond butter
As desired	honey
Dash	cinnamon/nutmeg or turmeric

Method

In a saucepan, roast the flour on medium heat while stirring constantly for 2-5 minutes until a nutty aroma is achieved (the longer you roast, the nuttier the final flavor becomes). Add water, rice milk and stir, making sure to avoid any clumps. Bring to a boil then remove from heat. Serve topped with tahini, honey, and a pinch of cinnamon/nutmeg.

Chilled Porridge

Ingredients

2/3 cup	precooked buckwheat, teff, or amaranth
1 cup	rice milk
1/3 cup	fresh or frozen blueberries
2 tbsp	almond or walnut pieces
1 tsp	un-pasteurized honey (optional)

Method

Mix cooked grains with rice milk and honey overnight, and keep refrigerated in a sealed container as this will keep the grains soaked.
When serving, top with blue berries and almonds, and enjoy.

Variations

The nuts can be replaced with seeds, such as sunflower or pumpkin seeds.
The nuts can be added to the mix overnight for a softer texture.
Papaya or mango purée can replace the berries.
Fresh pitted black dates can be substituted for the honey.

Puffed Grain Cereal

Ingredients

1 cup	puffed rice, millet, or amaranth (found in most healthfood stores)
1 cup	rice milk or almond milk
1 tsp	your choice of nuts or seeds
1 tsp	un-pasteurized honey (optional)
1/3 cup	frozen berries

Method
Place ingredients in a bowl and enjoy.

**Sprout Cereal*

Ingredients

1/3 cup	sunflower sprouts
1/3 cup	mung bean sprouts
1	mango cut in chucks
1.5 cup	rice milk
2	dried figs, cut in small chunks
2 tsp	ground walnuts

Method
Separate sprouts so that the sprouts are not clumped together.
Place sprouts in a bowl and top with mangoes.
Blend dates and rice milk. Pour the blend into the bowl and enjoy.
Alternatively you can chop the dates.

Variations
Rice milk can be replaced with almond milk or other allowed nut milks.
Other fruits such as frozen berries or papaya chunks can replace the mangoes.
Raisins or dates can be used instead of the figs.
You can top the dish with your choice of nuts.
Red clover sprout can replace mung bean sprouts.

Pancakes

Ingredients

3 tbsp	buckwheat, teff, or quinoa flour
2/3 cup	water or rice milk
2 tsp	ground or chunks of walnuts/almonds
2 tsp	raisins
Pinch	sea salt
2 tbsp	frozen berries
As desired	un-pasteurized honey
Dash	cinnamon
1 tbsp	coconut oil (for frying)

Method

Mix the flour into the rice milk; add sea salt and coconut milk and whip. Add nuts, and cook batter on a hot oiled coconut oil frying pan, making sure to spread it thinly (as it takes longer for teff or buckwheat flour to cook, relative to wheat flour). When ready, flip pancakes.

Serve topped with a small amount of honey, blueberries, and a dash of cinnamon.

Variations

For variations, try adding berries, or grated pear to the batter, or top the pancakes with your choice of toppings.

Hummus Avocado Spread

Use bread made with any of the alternative grain flowers (make sure the restricted grains are not in the ingredient list).

Spread hummus and top with sliced or mashed avocados.
Enjoy with grapes and a cup of fresh juice or green tea.

Savory Spread

Use bread made with any of the alternative grain flour (make sure the restricted grains are not added), or rice puffs.

Spread tahini (sesame butter) and top with any combination of sardines (in olive oil), sliced black olives, cucumbers, or avocadoes, salt and pepper. Enjoy with a cup of lemon mint tea, or fresh juice.

Variation
Sardines can be replaced with canned salmon or herring.

Sweet Spread

Use bread made with any of the alternative grain flours, or rice puffs. Spread with un-pasteurized honey and pumpkin seed butter or almond butter. Enjoy with a side of green tea or ginger tea.

Amaranth Flatbread

(Makes two 30 cm by 20 cm flat breads)
Ingredients
1 cup	amaranth flour
1 cup	water
Dash	baking soda
Dash	sea salt
1 tbsp	coconut or olive oil (for greasing pan)

Method
Mix ingredients, spread thinly (as thin as possible), on a greased (coconut oil, or olive oil) baking pan. Bake at 350F in a preheated oven for 5-15 minutes (cooking time varies with thickness of batter).

Date Spread

Ingredients

8-10	pitted black dates (i.e. fresh dates)
1/4 cup	coconut milk (optional)
1/2 tsp	ground cardamom
2 tsp	walnut pieces
As needed	water
Dash	sea salt
Dash	cinnamon
1-2 tsp	coconut oil (for frying)

Method

Heat coconut oil in a pan. Add dates, and fry on medium heat for 1-2 minutes. Add coconut milk and walnut pieces into the pan, and stir constantly. Add cardamom and a dash of sea salt, and stir in. If necessary add water and stir in until a creamy consistency is achieved.

Chill and serve on rice crisps, amaranth flatbread, or breads made of any of the allowed grains.

Note

This recipe also makes a great addition as a side garnish for heavy protein dishes.

If using dried dates you may need to add water several times while stirring to get the creamy consistency. It may also be advisable to soak the dates in water in advance

Snacks

Shakes

For the following recipes, place all ingredients in a blender, and blend.
If using fresh fruits, add 2 to 3 ice cubes into the blender to get a thick and creamy consistency.

As an option; you can add a heaping teaspoon of brown rice protein or pea protein powder to any of the shakes.
You may also add a teaspoon of flaxseed oil or other sources of essential fats.

Very berry
2/3 cup of frozen mixed berries
handful of mixed nuts
2 seedless dates or 1 tbsp of honey
1 tsp flax seed oil (optional)
1 cup of rice milk, (or half water half rice milk)

Nutty delight
1 pitted dates
2 dried figs
2 tsp of ground flax seeds
3 walnuts
1 tsp tahini (or pumpkin seed butter)
1 cup almond milk/ rice milk

*Mango berry
1/2 cup fresh or frozen mangoes
1/2 cup fresh of frozen blueberries
6-8 almonds/walnuts
1 tsp flaxseed oil
1 cup rice milk, or almond milk

Mango tango
1 fresh Mango, peeled, seeded, and cut into chunks
6-7 almonds, or 2 tsp almond butter
1/3 tsp of turmeric (optional)
1 tsp flax seed oil
2 ice cubes
1 cup rice milk, or almond milk

Papaya and mango
1/2 cup fresh or frozen papayas
1/2 cup fresh or frozen mangoes
2 tsp pumpkin seed butter, or sesame seed butter (Tahini)
1 tsp flax seed oil
1 cup rice milk, or almond milk

*Avocado and dates
1 avocado, skinned and pitted
3 walnuts
2 or 3 pitted dates (or 1 teaspoon un-pasteurized honey)
2-3 ice cubes
1 cup rice milk, or almond milk

Fresh Vegetable Juices

A juicer is needed for the following recipes. Alternatively you can get them at a juice stand.
The quality of the nutrients is reduced if the juice is pasteurized or packaged, or if it is left sitting for more than 1/2 hr after juicing.

Fresh juices can be refrigerated in a sealed airtight bottle for up to 3 days. When making combinations of fruits and vegetables, the juice may not last as long.

Carrot-celery-beet
4 carrots, 3 celery stalks, 1 beet
Mix in 1 teaspoon of turmeric powder.

*Apple-carrot-ginger
2 apples (seeded), 4 carrots, 1 cm of fresh ginger.

Beet red
1 med beet, with beet greens
2 carrots
1/3 cucumber
1 pear or apple (seeded)

*Very green
Handful of spinach and parsley
1/2 average broccoli
2 celery stalks
1/4 average sized kale (stems and leaves)
1/3 cucumber
1 pear (seeded)

Purple cabbage
4 leaves of red cabbage
2 carrots
1/3 cucumber
1 pear (optional)

Any creative combination of fresh vegetables and fruits.

Snack Ideas

Fruits: Whole fresh fruits. Best chosen according to the season (raisins, dates and dried figs are allowed).

Any combination of nuts and seeds: Nuts have a high fat, protein and fiber content. You are recommended to make this snack a part of your everyday life as it is the most ancient source of human nutrition.

Juices: Any fresh fruit or vegetable juices (unsweetened)

Shakes: Any of the above recipes.

Vegetable Sticks: Cucumber sticks dipped in almond butter, pumpkinseed butter, sesame seed butter (tahini), or hummus.
Slightly steamed celery or carrot sticks (2-3 min of steaming is enough to make them digestible).

Rice cracker/ rice puffs/ rice cakes with hummus, natural dip, or nut butter. Make sure the nut butter is non-hydrogenated. In non-hydrogenated nut butters, the nut oil naturally separates and forms a layer on top of the nut butter.

*Avocado halves: Cut an avocado into two. Remove the seed, but leave the skin on. Sprinkle both halves with a dash sea salt and dash of cumin or turmeric. Squeeze a fresh slice of lime onto both halves. Use a spoon to scoop the avocado flesh, and enjoy.

Amaranth popcorns: Amaranth seeds can be toasted until they pop like popcorn.

Fruit salads: Any combination of allowed fruits.

Finally: Pay a visit to your natural health food store, you will be surprised by the number of alternative snack you have available to you.

Sauce for fruit salad

Ingredients

1/2	fresh squeezed lemon
1 tsp	almond butter, or sesame butter (tahini)
1-2 cm	graded ginger

Method
Mix and pour over fruit salad.

Dips

Bean dip

Ingredients

1 cup	cooked kidney beans
1 cm	ground fresh ginger
1/4 cup	papaya chunks
2 tbsp	tahini (sesame butter)
1/4 cup	finely cut sweet onions (spanish, red, or pearl)
2 tbsp	olive oil
1 tsp	ground cumin
Handful	finely chopped basil
To taste	sea salt

Method

Mash the beans, and mix all ingredients (except for the basil) in a bowl. Top with basil, and enjoy with rice crackers, rice puffs, or cucumber sticks.

Variation

Kidney beans can be substituted with any other beans.

Papaya can be replaced by pineapple (both papaya and pineapple have digestive enzymes that can help with the digestion of the beans)

Other herbs such as cilantro, parsley, dill, or mint can substitute basil.

Avocado Dip

Ingredients

2	avocados, peeled, pitted, and diced
1/2	fresh lime, juiced
2 tsp	olive, or flax oil
1/2 tsp	ground fennel seeds
1/4 cup	pitted-black olives, sliced
Handful	finely chopped cilantro
Handful	finely chopped green onion
As needed	sea salt

Method
In a bowl, mash the avocados, and mix in the ingredients. Save some of the cilantro for garnish.
Enjoy with rice crackers, cucumber, or rice puffs.

Variations
Chopped garlic can be added.

Hummus

Ingredients

2 cups	precooked chickpeas
1	lime, fresh squeezed
3 tbsp	sesame seed butter (tahini)
1/4 cup	finely chopped parsley, celery stalk, or coriander
2 - 4	cloves of garlic, finely chopped
1/4 cup	olive oil
1 tsp	ground cumin
1/2 tsp	turmeric powder (optional)
1/2 tsp	ground fennel
1 tsp	black pepper
To taste	sea salt

Method

Place and blend all ingredients in the blender/food processor.

Chill for 30 minutes and enjoy with rice crackers, cucumbers, or lightly steamed celery or carrot sticks.

Or use as a spread on top of any bread made from allowed grains.

Cauliflower Dip

Ingredients

1/2 head	cauliflower, roughly chopped
1 cup	water
3 tsp	olive oil
1/2 tsp	turmeric
Dash	black pepper
To taste	sea salt

Method

Place cauliflower in a sauce pan, add small amount of water, and steam on medium heat for 5 minutes.

Place steamed cauliflower with the rest of the ingredients in a food processor and blend.

Chill for 30 minutes and enjoy with rice crackers, cucumbers, or lightly steamed celery, carrot, or broccoli sticks.

Herbs And Chickpea Dip (or as a Pie Filling)

Ingredients

1/2 cup	chickpea flour
2 cups	water
1 cup	fresh parsley, minced
1 cup	fresh cilantro, minced
1/2 cup	fresh basil, minced
1/4 cup	fresh tarragon, minced
1/4 cup	fresh mint, minced
4 stalks	scallions (green onion)
2 tsp	turmeric
1 tsp	black pepper
1 tsp	sea salt
2 tsp	coconut oil

Method

Slowly mix the chickpea powder into the water making sure no clumps are formed. Add the herbs, spices and sea salt and mix.

Grease the baking pan with coconut oil. Spread the mixture in the pan and bake at 350F for 30 minutes.

This mixture makes an excellent filing for any **pie dish** made with allowed grains flowers.

Soups, Congees And Chili

(All recipes make 4-6 servings)

Butternut Yellow Soup

Ingredients

3 cups	butternut squash, in chunks.
2	onions, thin sliced
8	garlic cloves (4 lightly chopped, 4 whole)
2	carrots, peeled and chopped
1/2 cup	ground walnut/pecan
4cm	ginger, peeled and grinded
2 tsp	un-pasteurized honey (optional)
2/3 cup	olive oil
2 tsp	dried basil (crushed)
2 tsp	dried mint (crushed)
2 tsp	cumin powder
As needed	sea salt

Method

Place squash, carrots, and 4 whole cloves of garlic in 6 cups of water and bring to a boil. Boil for 15 minutes or until carrots are slightly tender. Purée using a food processor. Reduce the heat and add 1/3 cup of olive oil, sea salt, basil, cumin, ginger, ground nuts, and honey (optional). Simmer for another 20 minutes. If soup is too thick, add sufficient water to get a nice smooth texture.

In a saucepan, heat olive oil, and sauté the onions and garlic. When onions turn soft, add sea salt and crushed mint. Stir for 3-4 minutes.
Ladle soup into serving bowls and garnish with sautéed onions and garlic.

Beet And Bok Choy Soup

Ingredients

1 1/4 cups	chickpeas (presoaked)
9 cups	water
3	medium beets, cut in 4 and thin sliced
2 cups	bok choy, coarsely chopped. (approximately 4 stalks)
1	onion, thin sliced
4	garlic cloves, sliced
1 1/2 cups	fresh dill, coarsely chopped (about 1/2 bunch)
2 tsp	ground fennel seeds
1 tsp	black pepper
1 tsp	turmeric
1/2 cup	olive oil
As needed	sea salt
To taste	balsamic vinegar

Method

Soak chickpeas in water overnight. Drain the water and place the chickpeas in a pot with 9 cups of water. Bring to boil, add the rest of the ingredients (except bob choy and dill), cover and boil on low heat for 1 hour. Add bok choy and dill, cover and boil for another 30 minutes.

Ladle into a bowl sprinkle with balsamic vinegar to taste.

Variation

If using canned chickpeas, you can cut the cooking time in half: Cook beets with the rest of ingredients for 20 minuets. Then add the bok choy and dill and boil for another 10 minutes. Finally, drain , rinse, and add canned chickpeas and boil for a final 10 minuets before serving

Split Pea Soup

Ingredients

6-7 cups	water
1.5 cups	green split peas (rinsed)
2/3 cup	cauliflower, chopped
2	celery stalks, thinly sliced
1	medium carrot, peeled and chopped
1	onion, chopped
6	garlic cloves, thinly sliced
4 cm	fresh ginger, ground
2 tsp	dried thyme
1.5 tsp	ground cumin
1 tsp	black pepper
1 tbsp	olive oil (for sautéing)
2 tsp	sea salt

Method

In a deep pot, sauté onions in olive oil with black pepper, using medium heat. When onions turn soft add split peas and stir for 3-4 minutes. Add 6 cups of water, sea salt and bring to a boil. Boil for 20 minutes on medium heat and then purée the contents. Add the rest of the ingredients and boil for another 20 minutes. If the soup is too thick, adjust the consistency by adding one more cup of water.

Green Spinach Soup

Ingredients

7 cups	water
1 cup	red lentils (rinsed)
2 cups	spinach, coarsely chopped
2 cups	red cabbage, thinly sliced (5-6 medium leaves)
1	onion
4	garlic cloves, minced
1 tsp	ground cumin
1 tsp	turmeric
1 tsp	dried ground basil
2 tsp	fresh thyme
1/2 cup	olive oil
As needed	sea salt

Method

In a deep pot, sauté onions and garlic with olive oil. Add 7 cups of water and the rest of the ingredients (except red cabbage and spinach), and bring to a boil. Boil on medium for 20 minutes. Add spinach and cabbage and boil for another 20 minutes.

Wild Rice And Turnip Soup

Ingredients

4	medium turnips, skinned and sliced
1/2 cup	wild rice
1	onion, chopped
5	cloves of garlic, chopped
2 cups	collards, coarsely chopped (can use any other leafy green vegetable)
1	sweet potato, chopped.
1 cup	parsley, minced
4 tsp	fresh rosemary (approx 4 stalks)
1 tsp	ground coriander seeds
1 tsp	ground fennel
1 tsp	cumin seeds
5 tsp	chickpea powder
2 tsp	sesame oil
1/2 cup	olive oil
To taste	sea salt

Soups

Method

In a deep pot, sauté the onions and garlic in olive oil, black pepper, and sea salt. Add turnips and 4 cups of water and bring to a boil. After 10 minutes of boiling, purée the mixture along with the rosemary, coriander seeds, fennel, and cumin seeds. Add the rest of ingredients (except for the sweet potatoes and parsley) to the onion-herbs-turnip purée (make sure to add the chickpea powder slowly so as not to clump). Add 4 more cups of water and bring to a boil. Boil for 20 minutes. Add sweet potato and parsley and cook for another 15 minutes.

Cumin Lentils (See Note)

Ingredients

2 cups	lentils, washed and drained
4	garlic cloves, sliced
1	medium onion, chopped
4 cm	ginger, thinly sliced
1/2 cup	olive oil
1 tsp	ground cumin
1 tsp	ground fennel
1 tsp	dried thyme
To taste	sea salt

Method

In a deep pot, sauté the onions, garlic, and ginger in olive oil on medium heat, until onions are soft and an aromatic flavor is released. Add lentils to the pot, along with 6 cups of water. Add the herbs (cumin, fennel, and thyme), and bring to a boil. Reduce heat and boil for 1.45 to 2 hrs.

Depending on the desired final texture you can increase or decrease the amount of water.

Note: This is a basic recipe that can be used for red beans, black beans or any other beans. Keep in mind that the cooking time is different depending on the kind of bean and the brand you buy, so check the cooking instructions. Also note that **when cooking beans you will need to pre-soak them over night.**

Variation

This recipe, regardless of the kind of beans/lentils you use, can be served in many ways:

Serve the lentils in a bowl, top with sprouts and canned tuna.

Mix a few spoons of the beans with your favorite salad. (kidney beans, and mung beans are good for this purpose)

Add green bok choy, spinach, carrots, brussel sprouts, and sesame oil, and you have a soup. (This soup would taste best with mung beans, also mung bean have a relatively short cooking time.)

Creamy Broccoli Fish Soup

Ingredients

200 grams	white fish fillet, cut into small chunks
1/2 cup	buckwheat flour
1	large onion, thinly sliced into 1/2 rings.
6	cloves of garlic, chopped
1 cup	parsley, finely chopped
1	large broccoli crown (stalk removed)
2 tsp	black pepper
1 tsp	dried thyme
1 tsp	dried dill
1 tsp	dried oregano
2 tsp	sesame oil
1/4 tsp	crushed mustard seeds
1/2 cup	olive oil
1/3 cup	coconut milk (optional)
2-3 tsp	sea salt

Soups

Method

Sauté onions and garlic in olive oil, with black pepper and sea salt. Add 6 cups of water, and slowly stir in the buckwheat flower. Bring to a boil. Add the rest of ingredients except for the fish, broccoli and sesame oil. Boil for 15 minutes and stir several times. Add the rest of ingredients and boil for another 20 minutes.

Variations

Brussel sprouts can replace broccoli. Use about 15-20 brussel sprouts and sauté in olive oil with onions, garlic, sea salt and black pepper.

Chili

Ingredients

1/2 cup	black beans (presoaked overnight)
1 cup	red kidney beans (presoaked overnight)
1/2 cup	black eyed beans (presoaked overnight)
1 cup	pomegranate juice
1/2 lb	ground lamb, or finely cut chunks
1	medium red onion, finely chopped
3	cloves of garlic, crushed
4 tbsp	coconut oil
1/3 bunch	finely chopped parsley
1	green onion, finely chopped
1	medium zucchini, sliced
2	medium carrots, washed, peeled, and chopped
1tsp	black pepper
1tsp	turmeric
1 tsp	ground cumin
As needed	sea salt

Method

Presoak the beans overnight. Drain water, rinse, and place in a pot with 7 cups of water, pomegranate reduction, sea salt, cumin, black pepper, and turmeric. (If using 1 cup of pomegranate juice, then use 6 cups of water instead.) Bring to a boil and cook on medium heat for 1 hour.

Meanwhile, in a frying pan, warm coconut oil and sauté the red onions and green onions on medium to low heat until onions turn soft and clear, but not brown. Add the ground lamb, dash of sea salt and stir until the meat turns brown. Put aside for the moment.

Once the beans are ready (after 1 hour), combine all the ingredients in the pot, and cook for another 45 minutes, or until the beans are soft.

Serve with some bread made from any of the allowed grains.

Chicken Leek Soup

Ingredients

2	chicken breasts, cut into pieces.
2	medium carrots, peeled and chopped
2	leek stalks, chopped
2	medium onions, chopped
6	garlic cloves, diced
1/2 cup	olive oil
1/3 cup	cranberries (fresh or frozen)
1.5 tsp	black pepper
3 tsp	dried crushed marjoram (or basil)
1 tsp	thyme (fresh or dried)
2 tsp	sea salt
4 tsp	of either arrowroot or buckwheat powder
2 tsp	minced parsley (for garnish)

Soups

Method

Sauté the chopped onions, leeks, and garlic in a pot containing olive oil, sea salt, and black pepper. Add chicken/turkey breasts and either arrowroot or buckwheat powder, and stir until the meat turns white. Add 7 cups of water, herbs (marjoram and thyme) and carrots and bring to a boil. Reduce to medium heat and cook for 20 minutes. Finally, add cranberries, and cook for another 15 minutes.

Garnish with minced parsley and serve.

Variations:

Leeks can be replaced by sliced cabbage.
Dried crushed nettle leaf can be used instead of parsley.
If chicken is not desired as a source of protein, it can be replaced by presoaked red or black beans.

Chicken Rice Congee

Ingredients

2/3 cup	white/ brown rice (rinsed)
1	small onion, cut.
1	clove garlic, finely chopped
1 (6-8 0z)	chicken breast, cut to small pieces or shreds.
6 cups	water
2 tbsp	olive oil
3 cm	fresh ginger, finely shredded
2	fresh plums, peeled, pitted, and cut to pieces
3 tbsp	parsley, minced (for garnish)
Pinch	turmeric (optional)
Pinch	black pepper
As needed	sea salt

Method

In a medium saucepan/pot, heat olive oil on medium heat, and sauté onions and garlic until onions are soft. Mix in the chicken breast and stir for 2-3 minutes.

Add rice, 6 cups of water, sea salt, turmeric, and black pepper to the pot and bring to a boil over high heat. Cover the pot. Reduce to low heat and simmer for 1 1/2 to 2 hours or until congee is thickened and the ends of the rice grains have split (blossomed). When ready, add ginger and plums, and simmer for another 5 minutes.

Ladle congee into soup bowls, and garnish with minced parsley.

Variation

Chicken can be replaced by lamb chops, or ground lamb. If so add a pinch of cumin for extra flavor.

Plums can be omitted or replaced by fresh plum purée or plum sauce. (Read labels to avoid any restricted ingredients.)

Vegetarian Congee

Ingredients

2/3 cup	white/ brown rice (rinsed)
1	small onion, chopped
1	clove of garlic, finely chopped
1/4 cup	black beans (presoaked overnight)
1	small carrot, cut in rings
3	baby bok choy, cut in 4 lengthwise
4 tbsp	olive oil
1 tsp	sesame oil
2 cm	fresh ginger, finely shredded
4 tsp	cilantro leaves, finely chopped (for garnish)
4 tsp	ground almonds (for garnish)
Pinch	black pepper
To taste	sea salt

Soups

Method

In a medium pot, heat olive oil on medium heat and sauté onions and garlic until onions are soft. Mix in the beans and stir for 5 minutes.

Add rice and 6 cups of water, sea salt, black pepper, and ginger to the pot, and bring to a boil over high heat. Cover the pot. Reduce to low heat, and simmer for 1 1/2 hours or until congee is thickened and the ends of the rice grains have split (blossomed).

When ready, add baby bok choy and sesame oil and simmer for another 5-7 minutes.

Ladle congee into soup bowls, and garnish with ground almonds and cilantro.

Basic grain recipes

Rice

Method
Rinse 1 cup of rice (brown or white).
Place with 2 1/2 cups of water in the pot.
Add 2 tbsp of olive oil.
Add 1 tsp of sea salt.
Bring to a boil.
Once most of the water is evaporated, decrease the heat to low. Cover and simmer for 12-18 minutes. Brown rice will require slightly more steaming time relative to white rice.

Variations
To get a distinct flavor and taste of the rice, try adding the following ingredients to the boiling water:

2 tbsp of tahini,
Or 1 tsp of sesame oil
Or 1/2 cup of coconut milk
Or 1/2 cup of organic sultana raisins
Or 1/2 cup of mango purée
Or 1 tsp of plum sauce
Or 2 tbsp of dried dill
Or 1/3 cup of fresh cranberries
Or 1 tbsp of dried basil or thyme
Or 2 cm shredded fresh ginger
Or 1 finely chopped clove of garlic
Or 1 tsp of ground cumin or fennel
Or 1/2 cup of mixed frozen chopped carrots and sweet green peas.
Or any combination of above ingredients

Quinoa And Teff

Method
Use two parts liquid to one part grain in a medium saucepan. Bring to a boil.
Add 2 tbsp of olive oil.
Add 1 tsp of sea salt.
Reduce to a simmer. Cover and cook about 15-18 minutes.

Variations
You can toast the grain in a dry skillet for five minutes before cooking to give it a delicious roasted flavor.

You can also add in the extra ingredients listed in the "variations" section of the rice recipe.

Amaranth

Method
Place 1 cup of seeds in 2 1/2 cups of water and bring to a boil. Cover and cook until seeds are tender (approximately 18 to 20 minutes).

Grains

Amaranth can also be used as a breakfast cereal, but you will have to increase the water to 3 cups, and sweeten with un-pasteurized honey or add raisins and some nuts.

Variations
See rice recipe
You can also mix in precooked beans.

Buckwheat

Method

Rinse 1cup buckwheat in a fine mesh strainer. Buckwheat tends to absorb water easily, so only rinse it briefly.

Bring 2 1/2 cups of water to a boil, and add in 1 tsp of sea salt and 2 tbsp of olive oil. Add buckwheat and reduce to low heat. Simmer covered and cook for 12 to 15 minutes. Check the buckwheat halfway; since the grain is porous and absorbs a lot of water, you want to make sure there is enough liquid to avoid burning the bottom of the pan. You may want to stir a couple of times.

Variations

To create a more warming dish you can toast the buckwheat for about 3 to 4 minutes before preparation.

You can also add in the extra ingredients listed in the "variations" section of the rice recipe.

Quick and Easy

Steamed Veggies

Ingredients

2	yams or sweet potatoes
2	medium carrots
2	turnips
1	broccoli crown
2 tsp	olive oil (optional garnish)
Pinch	cinnamon or ground nutmeg (optional garnish)

Method

Wash, peel and cut the vegetables into chunks.

Place in a steamer, and add 2 cups of water.

Steam for 10-15 min.

Place the vegetables in plate and enjoy with olive oil, and cinnamon/nutmeg on the yams.

This makes a versatile side dish on its own, or a complete meal with a side serving of hummus and slice of any alternative grain breads.

Variation

You can steam any combination of your favorite vegetables.

Quick, easy

Boiled Beets (And Turnips)

Wash and peel a few beets or turnips. Cut in halves or slices. Place in a pot with 1 cup of water. Bring to a boil. Cover and cook until soft. You may have to adjust the water if cooking more than 3 medium sized beets or turnips.

This makes a great snack, side dish or an addition to salads, especially in tossed green salads.

Baked Squash Or Pumpkin

Cut a whole squash in half. Remove the seeds. Place on a baking pan cut sides down. Bake at 350F for 35-45 min or until soft.
Sprinkle with cinnamon or nutmeg and enjoy with a splash of olive oil.

Quick Grain Dishes

(1-2 servings)
Ideal for left over grains, precooked grains.

Ideas:

1. Sautéed onions (1/2 onion), garlic, 1 canned tuna/salmon/herring /sardines (drain off the oil), lemon and dill.

2. Sautéed onions (1/2 onion), figs (raisins or dried organic cranberries), slivered almonds, scallion (2 tsp, chopped, garnish).

3. Sautéed onions (1/2 onion), spinach (1/2 cup, cut), walnuts (2 tbsp).

4. Sautéed onions (1/2 onion), chickpeas (1/2 cup precooked), mango purée (1/2 mango), slivered almonds (2 tbsp), cumin (1 tsp).

Method

Over medium heat, sauté 1/2 cup of onion chunks (and 2 minced garlic cloves) in olive oil until soft. Add the rest of ingredients, stir for 1-2 minutes.

In a separate pot warm up 1 cup of precooked grains on medium heat by with 2 tsp water. Cover and let steam for 3-5 minutes. Alternatively you can cook a new batch of your favorite grain.

Serve rice topped with the mixture and a side salad.

Stir-fry

(2-3 servings)

Ideas:

1. One onion (sliced), 1/2 cup green beans, 1 carrot (thinly sliced), 1 zucchini (sliced), 1/2 cup pineapple (pizza-shaped slices), 2 tbsp walnuts.

2. One onion (sliced), 4 garlic cloves (minced), 3 cups cauliflower (cut into small chunks), 1 zucchini (cut in slices), 3 tsp turmeric, 1.5 cup chickpeas (precooked)

3. One onion (sliced), 2 cups cabbage (thinly sliced), 1 broccoli (chopped), 2 tsp cumin, and 4 tbsp slivered almonds.

4. One sliced onion, 1/2 lb lamb meat (fat free, thin sliced), 1 broccoli head (cut into pieces), 2 tsp cumin, 1/2 bunch spinach cut in half.

5. One onion (sliced), 1 cup white fish chunks (fresh/frozen), 1 cup fresh green peas (in pod), 1/2 bunch asparagus with bottoms chopped off and cut into halves, 1 tsp dried dill, juice of 1 lime.

6. Any combination of your favorite vegetables, meat, and spices.

Quick, easy

Method

In a Wok or a deep frying pan, sauté onions or garlic over medium heat in 1/4 cup coconut oil until soft. Add the rest of the ingredients. Stir fry for about 1 minutes. Add small amount of water (less than 1/4 cup), sea salt, spices, and your choice of a dried herb (thyme, basil, marjoram, or oregano). And stir for 3-5 minuets.

Add another 1/4 cup of water, Stir for 1 minute, cover and lightly steam on medium heat for 3-5 minutes. Remove cover, stir for another minute or two.

Note that adding water to the oils keeps the temperature of stir-fry low and you can avoid creating toxic chemicals that generally are made as a result of frying.

All stir fries serve well over basic grain dishes, quinoa, teff, and buckwheat, garnished with nuts and sprouts.

Variation
You can add 1/2 cup of coconut milk to the stir-fry to give it a creamy texture.

With meat: You can stir in 1/2 to 1 cup of either chicken breast (thinly sliced), lamb (thinly sliced), or fish chunks into the sautéed onions; stir for a couple of minutes until the meat turns color, and then add the vegetables and follow the steps through.
Chicken goes well with any combination, but specifically with the 1st combination (especially when a handful of fresh/frozen cranberries are added immediately after the meat turns white).

Main course

(All main courses are 2-3 servings, unless otherwise indicated)

Sweet Quinoa Mix

Ingredient

1 cup	quinoa, rinsed
1	medium onion, sliced
1	pear, peeled and cut into small chunks
1/4 cup	raisins
1/2 tsp	ground cumin
2 tsp	fresh rosemary, chopped
1/2 tsp	ground black pepper
1/4 cup	sliced almonds
2 tsp	olive oil
As needed	sea salt
Handful	sunflower, bean, or alfalfa sprouts (as garnish)

Method
In a medium saucepan, bring 2 cups of water to a boil. Add quinoa, dash sea salt, raisins, and 1 tbsp olive oil. Bring to a boil, reduce heat, cover and simmer for 15 minutes.

Meanwhile, in a frying pan, on medium heat, sauté onions and rosemary in 1 tbsp olive oil, until onions are soft. Add the rest of the ingredients and stir for 3 minuets. Add cooked quinoa and stir for another 2 minuets.
Remove from heat, serve garnished with sprouts.

Variation
Pears can be replaced with mangos.

Mains

Ruby Chickpeas And Yam With Quinoa

Ingredients

1	yam/sweet potato
1	medium beet
1cup	pre-cooked chickpeas, (or canned)
1	cup Quinoa
1	small broccoli head cut in pieces
1tsp	cumin
1tsp	garlic powder
1/4 cup	olive oil
To taste	sea salt
Garnish	your choice of sprouts

Method

Wash, peel and cut the beets into 4 and slice into very fine thin slices. Wash and cut yams into chunks. Place the vegetables in a pot and pour 1 cup of water, a dash of garlic salt, and a dash of cumin. Cover and boil on medium flame for 15 min. Add the chickpeas/beans and heat for another 2 min.

Meanwhile place quinoa and 2 cups of water in a pot and bring to a boil. Add, salt, olive oil, reduce heat and simmer for 5 minutes. Stir in the broccoli, cover, and continue to simmer for another 5-7 min.

Serve chickpea/yam mixture on top of the quinoa.

Amaranth Grits

Ingredients

1 cup	amaranth
1	clove of garlic, finely chopped
1	scallion, snipped
1	medium onion, finely chopped
2	baby bok choy, cut in half
3 cups	water or vegetable stock
1 tsp	dried dill
1 can	tuna or salmon
1	lime, squeezed to taste.
To taste	sea salt

Method

In a medium saucepan/pot, heat olive oil on medium heat and sauté onions and garlic until onions are soft. Mix in amaranth and dried dill, and stir for 2-3 min. Add 1 cup of water or vegetable stock and bring to a boil. Reduce heat, cover and simmer for 15 minutes. Add bok choy, stir, and simmer for another 5-10 minutes. The amaranth should be crunchy, but not gritty hard.

Serve on a plate, topped with 1/2 can of tuna or salmon (room temperature or heated in a double boiler), and garnish with scallions, and flavor with limejuice.

Mains

Okra On Spinach Buckwheat

Ingredients

2/3 cup	buckwheat
2 cloves	garlic, minced
2 tsp	olive oil
1cup	spinach, chopped
1 cm	ginger, shredded
1/2 cup	coconut milk (optional, if not use 1/2 cup water)
1 med	onions, cut in thin half rings
2 stalks	scallion (green onions), chopped
1/2 cup	medium carrot, cut to thin slices, 1-2 inches long
2 cup	fresh okra, cut in half lengthwise
1 tbsp	coconut oil
1 tsp	turmeric powder
1 tsp	black pepper
Pinch	mustard seeds
To taste	sea salt

Method

Bring two cups of water to a boil. Add ginger, garlic, spinach, buckwheat, olive oil, and sea salt. Boil until most of the water evaporates. Reduce heat, cover and simmer for 15 minutes. You may need to stir a few times to avoid burning the bottom.

Meanwhile sauté carrots and onions, and mustard seeds in coconut oil, over medium heat. Add scallions and okra and stir for 3 minutes. Add 1/2 cup of water, coconut milk, turmeric powder, sea salt, and cook covered for another 10 minutes, stirring a few times.

Serve buckwheat in a deep bowl, topped with sautéed okra and carrots. Garnish with sunflower sprouts, and enjoy.

Variation

You can add thin chicken slices to the sautéed onions, stir for a couple of minuets until the meat turns color, and then follow instruction.

Alternatively you can add 1 cup of precooked chickpeas or beans to the recipe about 1 minuets before removing from heat.

Zucchini And Split Pea On Raisin Brown Rice

Ingredients

2/3 cup	split peas
5 stalks	scallion, chopped
3 cloves	garlic, minced
2 tsp	fresh mint, minced (or dry crushed mint)
1	zucchini, sliced along the length,
1 tsp	cumin
1/3 cup	cilantro, coarsely chopped
1 tbsp	pumpkin seed
2 tbsp	coconut oil
To taste	sea salt

Method

In a cooking pot, sauté scallion and garlic in 1 tbsp coconut oil, over medium heat. Add split peas, 2.5 cups of water, mint, cumin, and sea salt. Bring to a boil and cook on low heat for 30 minutes, stirring once in a while.

Meanwhile in a frying pan, stir fry zucchini in 1tbsp coconut oil and a small amount of water (sea salt to taste).

Serve on bed of raisin brown rice (prepared with 1/4 cup of raisins in 1 cup of brown rice), topped with split peas and zucchini, and garnished with fresh cilantro and pumpkin seeds.

Mains

Cabbage And Rice

Ingredients

1cup	brown rice, rinsed
2 cup	cabbage, sliced
1	large onion, cut into pieces
2 cloves	garlic, minced
pinch	saffron
4 tbsp	olive oil
1/2 tsp	turmeric powder
2 tsp	dried basil
To taste	sea salt

Method

In a saucepan, heat olive oil on medium heat to sauté the onions and garlic. Add cabbage, saffron, turmeric, basil, and sea salt. Stir for 4 minutes, remove from heat, and put aside.

In a deep pot bring 3 cups of water into boil. Add sea salt and brown rice and bring to a boil. When most of the water has evaporated (after about 7 minutes of boiling), stir in the cabbage mixture. Cover and simmer on low heat for 10-15 minutes.

Enjoy with a side of salad (with figs or raisins).

*Variation

You can add **ground lamb** to the sauté onions and stir until the meat turn color. And then add the cabbage, and continue.

Sweet Rice Lentils

Ingredients

1/2 cup	lentils (presoaked over night)
1 cup	brown rice, rinsed
1	medium onion, sliced
4 cloves	garlic, chopped
1 tsp	ground cloves
1/4 cup	raisins
1/4 cup	walnut chunks
1 tsp	olive oil
2 tsp	sea salt

Method

Presoak the lentils over night.

In a large pot, sauté the onion and garlic in olive oil until soft. Stir in the lentils, 3 cups of water, rice, sea salt, and cloves. Bring to a boil, stir in the raisins and nuts. When most of the water has evaporated, lower heat, cover and simmer for 30 minutes.

Serves well with a side of mango salad.

Mains

Brussels Sprouts And Pineapple Chicken

Ingredients

1	chicken breast, cut into chunks
10	brussels sprouts
3 tbsp	olive oil
2	garlic, finely chopped
1/2	red onion, sliced
1/4	pineapple, cut into pizza-shaped slices
1/2 tbsp	turmeric powder
1 tsp	sesame seeds
To taste	sea salt

Method

Sauté onions and garlic, over medium heat, in 2 tbsp olive oil and small amount of water. Add chicken breast and sea salt when onions turn soft. Stir for 3-5 minuets, until the meat turns color to white. Add in the pineapple and stir briefly and put the mixture aside.

Place brussels sprouts, 1/2 glass of water, and 1 tbsp olive oil into a deep pan. Cover and steam for 4-5 min at medium-high heat.

Reduce the heat to medium and mix in the chicken breast and pineapple into the pan. Add turmeric and stir on medium heat for 3-5 min.

Serve with sesame seeds on top.

You can enjoy this dish with a side of any allowed cereal grains.

Baked Chicken Breast

Ingredients

2	chicken breasts, cut in half
1	medium red onion, thinly sliced
4 cm	ginger root, ground
1 cup	fresh/frozen cranberries
1/2 cup	sultana raisins
3 tbsp	olive oil
2 tsp	dried crushed mint
1 tsp	black pepper
To taste	sea salt
1/2 cup	sunflower sprouts, or pea sprouts (garnish)

Method

Place the chicken breast in a baking pan. Sprinkle with a dash of sea salt and black pepper, and cover with half of the onion slices. Place in preheated oven, and bake at 350F for 20 minutes.

Meanwhile in a saucepan sauté the rest of onion slices in olive oil on medium heat. Stir in the rest of the ingredients. Add 2/3 cup of water, and cook on low heat for 7-10 minutes or until cranberries turn soft and crushed.

Pour sauce over the chicken breast and garnish with spouts.
Enjoy with a side of salad/brown rice.

Mains

Tamarind Turkey Breast

Ingredients

1/2	average turkey breast, cut in chunks
1	onion, sliced
4	cloves garlic
2	pears, shredded
1/2 cup	tamarind, pits removed (most Asian stores carry packaged fresh tamarind)
7	dried Fig, chopped
2tsp	coconut oil
1 tsp	black pepper
To taste	sea salt
Garnish	fresh, chopped thyme

Method

Place turkey breast in a baking pan with 1/4 cup of water and bake for 30 minuets in a preheated oven at 350F.

After 30 minuets of baking, blend tamarind, garlic, pears and 1 cup of water in a blender. Mix in the rest of the ingredients and pure the mixture over the turkey to cover all the chunks. Bake for another 20 minuets.

Remove from the oven. Garnish with fresh chopped thyme and serve with a side of your favorite grain dish (goes well with ginger brown rice, or ginger-thyme quinoa)

Chicken Pomegranate

Ingredients

2	chicken breasts, cut in 4
2	onions, cut into thin slices
2 cups	pomegranate juice
1/2 cup	olive oil
2/3-cup	ground walnuts
1.5 tsp	black pepper
1	medium cinnamon stick (optional)
To taste	sea salt
To taste	un-pasteurized honey
Garnish	tarragon leaf

Method

Sauté onions in olive oil until soft. Add chicken, salt and pepper, and stir until chicken turns color. Add the rest of ingredients and boil for 1/2 hr. Add extra water if the sauce is too thick. Add enough honey to balance the sour taste of pomegranate.

Serve on a bed of brown rice, and garnish with tarragon.

Mains

Grilled Salmon And Asparagus

Ingredients

2	wild salmon steaks
1	limes
6-10	asparagus, ends cut off
To taste	sea salt
Seasoning	dried crushed dill
1 tsp	coconut oil
1/3 cup	fresh or frozen raspberries

Method

Sprinkle the salmon steaks with salt and pepper, and sprinkle dried dill on top. Place on a baking pan and place in a preheated oven at 350F. Bake for 5-10 min. Squeeze 1/2 lime on each salmon steak, turn oven onto grill (500F) and grill for 10 min.

In a medium pan, heat coconut oil over medium heat and stir-fry asparagus for 3-5 minutes.

Serve with a side of dill rice, or dill buckwheat, and stir-fried asparagus topped with raspberries.

Variation

Any of you favorite fish fillet can replace salmon.

Herbed Halibut Steaks

Ingredients

2	halibut steaks
2 tsp	olive oil
1	scallion, finely chopped
1	fresh lemon, juiced
2 tbsp	fresh thyme, minced
1 tbsp	Dijon mustard
To taste	sea salt
Dash	ground black pepper

Method

Preheat oven to 350F. Sprinkle fish with sea salt, black pepper. Arrange in baking dish, and bake for 10 to 12 minutes.

When ready, mix lemon juice, mustard, olive oil and chopped thyme together in a small cup.

Place halibut steaks on a plate and pour mixture over fish.

Serve with side of flavored brown rice, salad or stir fried veggies.

Variation

Any of you favorite fish fillets can replace halibut.

Mains

Poached Whitefish And Raspberry Sauce

Ingredients

2	white-fish (or rainbow trout) fillets
1/2	scallion (green onion), finely chopped
1/2 tsp	dried dill
1/2 cup	raspberry, fresh or frozen
1	fresh lemon, juiced
1/2 tsp	honey
To taste	sea salt
Olive oil	

Method

Bring 2/3 cup of water to simmer in a saucepan. Place fillets (skin-side down) in the pan. Sprinkle with dill, and sea salt (to taste), cover and cook for 5-6 minutes on medium heat. Do not overcook.

Whip raspberries, lemon juice, olive oil, and honey in a bowl.

Serve fish on the plate, topped with raspberry sauce, and garnished with the scallions.

The Onion-Red-Cabbage stir-fry will be a good sidekick to this recipe. (See quick and easy recipes)

Steamed Yam And Baked Tuna

Ingredient

2	tuna steaks (can be replaced by canned tuna)
1tsp	crushed mint
1	lime
2	average-sized yams
1	turnip
1	broccoli, cut in chunks
To taste	sea salt
1 tsp	black pepper
To taste	olive oil
Dash	ground cinnamon

Method

Preheat oven to 350F. Place the tuna in a baking pan, and sprinkle with salt, pepper, and crushed mint. Cook for 7 min. Squeeze the juice of 1 fresh lime and crushed mint and bake for another 5 minutes.

Wash, peel, and chop the yam and turnip into large chucks. Place in a steamer. Steam for 10 min. Add broccoli and continue steaming for another 5 min. (alternatively you can stir fry the asparagus)

Serve on a plate, keeping the steamed yam separate. Sprinkle olive oil over the steamed veggies, and a dash of ground cinnamon on the yam only.

Enjoy with a side of any salad or grain dishes.

Variations

If using canned salmon or tuna, the heating time is 2-3 min.

Mains

Mango-Zest Smelt On Rice

Ingredients

1/2 lb	cleaned smelt or sardines, fresh or frozen
1	small onion, thin sliced
1	large mango, puréed
1.5 tsp	black pepper
4 cm	fresh grinded ginger
1	fresh squeezed lime.
1 tbsp	coconut oil

Method

Heat coconut oil in a deep pan or wok; add onions and sauté for 2 minutes or until soft. Add fish, salt, black pepper, and ginger, and fry on medium-high heat for 2-3 minuets (don't stir too much or else you will mash the fish). Pure lime juice and mango purée, decrease the heat and cook on low heat for 5-10 minuets. (If using canned sardines you can skip frying and just mix ingredients and pure mango puree over it before adding the mango purée)

Serve with a side of ginger flavored steamed brown rice and your choice of vegetable stir-fry or salad.

Variation

This is a versatile recipe. For those who are not found of the sardine taste, replacing the sardines with other small fish may be an ideal option.

Lamb Coconut Curry

(3-4 serving)

Ingredients

1/2 kg	boneless, low fat lamb meat chunks
2	onions, chopped
3 cloves	garlic, crushed
1	green mango, cut into thin long slices
8	dried figs, cut in chunks
4cm	fresh ginger, graded
1 can	coconut milk
1/3-cup	cilantro, diced
3 tbsp	coconut oil
1 Tbsp	turmeric powder
1 tsp	cumin powder
To taste	sea salt

Method

In a deep saucepan, sauté onions in coconut oil, until soft. Add lamb, sea salt, cumin, and turmeric powder, and stir until lamb chops turn color to brown. Add one cup of water, and bring to a boil. Cover and boil on medium heat for 30 minutes.

Add coconut milk and cilantro and boil for 15 minutes.

Add the rest of the ingredients and boil for another 10- 15 minutes.

Enjoy on a bed of brown rice, rice, or buckwheat, or other grains.

Variation

You can substitute the figs with 1/2 cup of raisins, or 1/2 cup of sliced pineapple.

Mains

Lamb Chunk With Celery And Herbs

(3-4 servings)

Ingredients

2 cups	lamb chunks
1	medium onion, chopped
4	cloves garlic, chopped
2 stalks	celery, cut in thin slices (0. 5 cm)
1/3 cup	mint, minced
1/3 cup	tarragon, minced
2/3 cup	cilantro, minced
2/3	parsley, minced
4 stalks	scallions, minced
1/4 cup	coconut oil
2 tsp	black pepper
2 tsp	sea salt

Method

In a deep pot, sauté onions and garlic in coconut oil until onions turns soft. Add the lamb chunks, sea salt, and black pepper and sauté for 2-3 minuets or until meat turns brown. Add herbs and celery and stir for 7-10 minutes over medium heat. Pour in 4 cups of water and bring to a boil. Cover and Boil on low heat for 45 minuets to 1 hr. If sauce is too thick, add more cup of water.

Serve on a bed of garlic flavored jasmine rice.

Cabbage And Lamb Steaks

Ingredients

2	lamb steaks
1/3-cup	fresh pineapples, cut into pizza chunks
3 cups	white cabbage, thinly sliced
1	onion, chopped
1/2 cup	olive oil
1 tsp	cumin powder
1 tsp	turmeric powder
To taste	sea salt
1 tsp	crushed dry rosemary
1 tsp	black pepper

Method

Marinate steaks by layering pineapple skin on both sides, for 1-2 hrs (optional, this will ensure the lamb is easily digestible as pineapples have digestive enzymes)

Sprinkle steaks with sea salt, pepper, and rosemary. Place in the oven at 350F, cook anywhere from 15-25 minutes to taste.

Meanwhile, sauté the onion and garlic in olive oil until onions are soft. Add cabbage, cumin, and turmeric, and stir on medium heat for 4-5 minutes. Add 1/2 cup of water and cover to steam for 5 minutes.

Serve steaks topped with 5-10 pineapple chunks and a side of cabbage stir-fry.

This dish will go well with green mango salad and a glass of mulled wine.

Mains

Lamb Shanks with Butternut Squash

(4 serving)

Ingredients

4	lamb shanks
1/2 cup	chickpeas, presoaked over night
2	large onion, coarsely chopped
10 cloves	garlic, 8 cut in half, 2 minced
1/3 cup	chopped parsley
8 cups	water
1 cup	red cooking wine (organic sulfite free, or 1 cup water)
3 tbsp	olive oil
1 tsp	cumin
1 tsp	thyme
1/4 tsp	saffron
2 tsp	turmeric
4	bay leafs
3 lbs	butternut squash, peeled and cut in half
To taste	black pepper
To taste	sea salt

Method

Sauté onions and minced garlic in a deep pot. Add lamb shanks, 1 teaspoon of sea salt and stir for 5 minutes until the meat turns color. Mix all other ingredients (except for the squash). Bring to a boil. Reduce heat, let cook for 2.5-3 hrs on medium heat.

About 1/2 hr before it is ready, place the squash halves on a cooking plate, cut sides down. Heat oven at 350F and bake squash for 1/2 hr or until soft. Top with olive oil, and serve on a plate next to lamb shanks.

Pasta Sauces

For all pasta dishes, in a large pot, bring 6-10 cups of water to a boil. Add, 2-4 servings of alternative grain pasta, 2-4 tablespoons of olive oil, 2-4 tsp sea salt, and cook according to package directions, or until soft but not sticky (15 to 25 minuets of boiling depending on pasta). Strain, and serve topped with your choice of sauce.

(All sauces are 2-4 serving)

Fresh Basil Pesto Recipe

Ingredients

2 cups	fresh basil leaves, coarsely chopped
1/3 cup	white wine
2 tsp	chickpea flour
1/2 cup	olive oil
1/3 cup	pine nuts (or walnuts)
3 cloves	garlic, skinned
1/2 tsp	sea salt
1/2 tsp	black pepper
Garnish	tahini (sesame butter)

Method

Place wine in a pot, bring to a boil, and boil for 5 minutes until most of the alcohol has evaporate. Remove from heat and put aside to cool.

When wine has cooled down, place all ingredients (except for tahini) in a food processor and blend. The pesto is ready.

Mains

Top pasta (linguine) with the freshly made pesto sauce, and sprinkle some tahini on top.

Spinach And Walnut In Pomegranate Squash Sauce

Ingredients

1 cup	butternut squash or pumpkin chunks
2 cups	pomegranate juice
2	garlic cloves, minced
6	scallions, minced
1 bunch	spinach, coarsely cut
1/3 cup	parsley, minced
4 tbsp	walnut, chunks, approximately 6-8 walnuts
2 tsp	dried basil, heaping
1/2 cup	pitted sliced black olives
1 tbsp	coconut oil
To taste	sea salt
Garnish	olive oil

Method

Place squash in a cooking pan with 1/2 cup of water. Bring to boil and cook for 10 minutes.

Place cooked squash in a blender with pomegranate juice and blend. Keep aside (alternatively you can mash the pumpkins into the pomegranate juice).

In a deep saucepan, heat coconut oil on med heat. Sauté garlic and scallions (1-2 minutes), with salt and pepper. Add spinach, parsley, and walnuts. Sauté until spinach is soft. Add dried basil and squash-pomegranate sauce. Stir and cook on medium heat for 10-15 minutes, or until a creamy texture is achieved.

Serve on top of a bed of brown rice, and top with black olives and fresh olive oil.
And garnish with walnut chunks.

Zucchini And Green Peas In White Wine-Mango Sauce

Ingredients

1	zucchini, cut into thin slices
2 cloves	garlic, finely chopped
1	red onion, cut into large half moon slices
1/2 cup	fresh green pea pods
1	medium, hard mango cut into chunks
1 cup	chickpeas, precooked (or canned)
2 cups	white wine
2 tbsp	chickpea powder
1/2 tsp	dried rosemary
1/2 tsp	dried thyme
1/2 tsp	ground cumin
1/2 tsp	turmeric
1 tsp	black pepper
3 tbsp	slivered almonds
1 tbsp	coconut oil
To taste	un-pasteurized honey
To taste	sea salt
Garnish	fresh mint leaves

Method

Place wine in a pot and boil for 10 minutes until most of the alcohol has evaporated. Reduce heat and put aside.

Heat coconut oil in a deep saucepan. Sauté garlic on medium heat until aroma is released. Add onions, zucchini, and green beans. Sauté on medium heat for 2-3 minutes while stirring .

Add wine, chickpea powder, mango chunks, herbs, and salt. Bring to a boil and cook for 1-2 minutes. If the sauce is too thick, add enough water to make it runny. Reduce heat, add chickpeas, the rest of the ingredients and enough honey to get a sweet flavor to the sauce and cook for another 2-3 minutes. (Depending on the sweetness of the wine you may need 2-4 tbsp of honey).

Serve on top of brown rice pasta and garnish with mints.

Mains

Creamy Chicken Lemongrass Pad-Thai

Ingredients

1/3 lb	Thai rice noodles (or brown rice linguine)
1/2	chicken breast, thinly sliced
1	medium red onion, sliced
1	stalks lemongrass, cut.
1	medium broccoli head, cut in chunks
1	medium carrots, thin sliced
1/2 cup	coconut milk
3 tbsp	coconut oil
1 tbsp	olive oil
1 tsp	black pepper
1	lime, freshly squeezed
To taste	sea salt
2 tsp	fresh mint, chopped (garnish)

Method

Bring 8 cups of water to boil in a deep pot. Add rice noodles, dash sea salt, and 1 tbsp olive oil. Boil for 15-20 minuets or until noodles are soft. Remove from heat, and drain the water.

Meanwhile, sautée onions and lemon grass in coconut oil. Add chicken chunks, and sauté until meat turns white. Add the rest of ingredients, plus 1 cups of water. Reduce the heat and boil off until a creamy texture is achieved. Mix in noodles. Stir for 1-2 minuets.
Serve garnished with fresh mint.

Herbed Salmon Macaroni

Ingredients

2 salmon	6 oz. salmon steaks, cut into chunks / or 2 cans of
5 cm pieces.	asparagus sticks, bottoms removed and cut into 4
1	onion, thin sliced
2	garlic cloves
1 tsp	fresh/or dried rosemary
4 tsp	fresh/or dried dill
2 tsp	fresh parsley minced
1/3 cup	olive oil
2 cups	quinoa or white rice macaroni
To taste	lemon, fresh squeezed
To taste	sea salt
To taste	black pepper

Method

Sauté onion and garlic in olive oil on medium heat in a sauce pan. Add fish, asparagus sticks, 1/3 cup of water, salt, pepper, and the herbs. Stir-fry until fish turns color.

In a separate pot, cook macaroni in boiling water until soft but slightly firm, then drain.

Mix all ingredients in the pot and stir on medium heat for 1-2 minutes. Season with lemon juice to taste.

Variation

This recipe can be served as a salad if chilled. Serve on top of iceberg lettuce leaves. You can replace salmon with other fish.

Mains

113

Salads

Salads are great source of vegetables in the diet.

(All salads are 2-3 serving)

Baby Spinach And Beet Salad

Ingredients

2 cups	baby spinach
1/2 cup	sliced cooked beets
1/4 cup	green onion sliced
2 tsp	sliced almonds
2 tbsp	raisins

Dressing

2 tbsp	olive oil
1/2	fresh squeezed lime juice
1/2 tsp	sea salt

Method

Peel and slice 2 medium beets, and place in 1 cup of boiling water. Cover pot and cook 20 minutes on medium heat. Chill beets. And mix with the rest of ingredients.

Raspberry Baby Spinach Salad

Ingredients

3 cups	baby spinach, washed, and dried
1/2	small red onion, thin sliced
2 tbsp	slivered almonds (garnish)

Dressing

1 cups	raspberry, fresh or de-frosted if frozen
1 tsp	honey
2 tbsp	balsamic vinegar
1 tsp	olive oil

Method

Mix ingredients in a large bowl. Whip/blend the dressing in a small bowl/blender and pour into salad. Garnish with almonds and enjoy.

Chickpea Basil Salad

Ingredients

1 can	chickpeas, drained and rinsed
1 cup	diced cucumber
1/2	sliced red onion
4 leaves	leaf lettuce, sliced
1/2	small endive, chopped
1/3 cup	minced basil

Dressing

1/2 tsp	mustard seed crushed
1 tbsp	olive oil
3 tbsp	apple cider vinegar

Method

Mix ingredients in a bowl. Whip together and pour dressing over salad.

Salads

Red Tuna Salad

Ingredients

4	leafs of leaf lettuce, sliced
1/2	can of tuna, flaked
1	pear, peeled and sliced
2 tbsp	ground pecans/walnuts
1/3	beet shredded

Dressing

1 tbsp	olive oil
1/2 tsp	sesame seed oil
1 tbsp	apple cider vinegar
1/2 tsp	Dijon mustard (organic, sulfite free)

Method

Mix lettuce, pears, nuts, and beets. Top with flaked tuna. Whip dressing together and top salad.

Variation

Tuna can be replaced by any other source of protein such as 1/2 cup cooked chickpeas, green beans, or red beans.

Tossed Greens And Avocado Salad

Ingredients

3 cups	mixed greens
1	avocado, peeled, pitted and cut in chunks

Dressing

To taste	olive oil
To taste	balsamic vinegar
Dash	ground cumin

Method

Toss the mixed greens in a bowl. Pour olive oil and vinaigrette over the salad, and top with raisins and a dash of cumin.

Mint Quinoa Salad

Ingredients

3 cups	precooked quinoa
1 can	black beans, rinsed
1 small	red sweet onion, sliced
1/2 cup	green or black olives, chopped
1/2	cucumber, peeled and minced
1/3 cup	slivered almonds
1/3 cup	parsley, minced
1/3 cup	chopped fresh mint
1	lime, fresh squeezed juices
3 tbsp	olive oil
2 tsp	ground cumin
1 tsp	sea salt

Method

Mix ingredients, chill for 10-20 minutes, serve.

**Cucumber Olive Vinaigrette Salad*

Ingredients

1/2 cup	black olives, sliced
1	large cucumber, peeled & thin sliced
1/3 cup	fresh cilantro, finely chopped
1/4 cup	fresh mint leaves, coarsely chopped (or fresh dill)

Dressing

3 tsp	olive oil
2 tbsp	balsamic vinegar
1 tsp	Dijon mustard

Method

Mix the first 4 ingredients in a large bowl. Mix and stir the dressing and pour over the salad.

Salads

Tossed Green And Lima Beans

Ingredients

3 cups	mixed greens
1/2 cans	lima beans, drained
3 tbsp	sunflower seeds or pumpkin seeds
1/3 cup	fresh pineapple, sliced (or 1/3 cup raisins instead)

Dressing

1 tbsp	tahini
4 tsp	olive oil
1/2	fresh lime, juiced
1 tsp	dry crushed basil
1 tsp	dry crushed mint
Sea salt	to taste

Method

Mix ingredients in a large bowl. Whip the dressing in a small cup and pour on top of the salad.

Variations

Pineapples can be replaced with fresh mango or pear slices.

*Mung Bean Cucumber Salad

Ingredients

2/3 cup	precooked mung beans
1/2	cucumber, chopped
1/4 cup	red olives, chopped
1/2	small sweet onion, sliced
1 cup	radicchio, sliced

Dressing

To taste	balsamic vinegar
To taste	olive oil

Method

Mix ingredients (except radicchio) in a bowl. Top with radicchio and dressing and enjoy.

Green Mango Salad

Ingredients

2	large hard mango, thin long sliced.
1	medium red onion, cut in half and sliced.
3	green scallion, cut to thin long slices.
2 tbsp	fresh coriander, minced

Dressing

1 tbsp	apple cider vinegar
1	fresh squeezed lime
1 tsp	sesame seed oil
1 tbsp	olive oil
1/2 tsp	un-pasteurized honey
To taste	Sea salt

Method

Mix ingredients in a bowl. Whip dressing together and pour over salad. Serve chilled.

Seaweed Salad

Ingredients

2 cups	fresh or thawed frozen green seaweed

Dressing

1 tsp	sesame seed
1tsp	sesame oil
2 tsp	olive oil
1 tsp	ground ginger (or dried powdered ginger)
1/2	fresh squeezed lime
Dash	black pepper
Dash	sea salt

Method

Mix ingredients in a bowl. Whip dressing together and pour over salad.

Salads

Watercress Figs Salad

Ingredients

1.5 cup	watercress, cut
1	medium endives, thinly sliced
1/2 cup	alfalfa sprouts, separated
2 tbsp	slivered almonds
4	dried figs, cut into pieces

Dressing

1/2	avocado, puréed
1 tsp	fresh rosemary, minced
1/2	fresh squeezed lemon
3 tsp	olive oil
1/2 tsp	ground cumin

Method

Mix ingredients in a bowl. Whip dressing together and pour over salad.

Head Lettuce And Kiwi Salad

Ingredients

1/2	head lettuce, cut
1	shredded carrot
1/2	cucumber, peeled & thin sliced

Dressing

1 tbsp	balsamic vinegar
2 tbsp	olive oil
1	skinned kiwi, minced
1 tsp	fresh thyme, minced
1 cm	peeled ginger, ground

Method

Mix ingredients in a bowl. Whip dressing together and pour over salad.

Desserts

Berry Slurp

(2 servings)

Ingredients

1 cup	frozen mixed berries
1/2 cup	chilled mango juice
`4-5	fresh mint leafs
1 tbsp	walnut chunks (garnish)

Method

Blend the berries, fruit juice and mint in a food processor. Pour into ice-cream cup garnish with walnuts.

Blueberry Freeze

(1 serving)

Ingredients

1cup	frozen blueberries
1/2 cup	rice milk

Method

Place frozen blue berried in a bowl and pour rice milk on top. Let it sit for 1-2 minutes, mix and enjoy.

Desserts

Arrow Root Pudding

(3-4 servings)
Ingredients

1/2 cup	arrowroot flour
1/2 cup	rice milk
1/4 cup	sesame seeds or ground almonds
1/4 cup	raisins
2 tbsp	honey
Pinch	ground cumin (optional)

Method

In a sauce pan, mix the flour into 2 cups of water. Add the rest of the ingredients and bring to boil on medium-high heat (make sure you constantly stir the mixture as the arrowroot will suddenly turn thick and can get sticky and burn the pot).

Once the texture has turned thick, remove from the heat, and serve in individual bowls, either chilled, or hot.

Glazed Pear pudding

(3-4 servings)

Ingredients

1/2 cup	arrowroot flour
2 cup	water
2	pears, peeled, cut in chunks
1	mango, peeled, cut in chunks
1/2	lemon, freshly juice
1/4 cup	ground almonds
Pinch	sea salt
To taste	un-pasteurized honey

Method

Mix arrowroot flour, and a pinch of salt in water, and leave aside for 15 minuets.

Meanwhile peel and core pears and mango and cut into chunks and distribute in 4 small bowls (you will be baking the mixture so use Pyrex bowls). Mix in lemon juice, honey, and ground almonds to the arrowroot mix and pour over fruit. Sprinkle with honey and bake at 350F for 20-30 minuets, or until pears are tender. Remove, chill, and serve.

Dessert

Blueberry Scones

(10-12 serving)
Ingredients

4 tsp	ground flax seed
1.5 cup	boiling water
2 cups	brown rice flour
4 tsp	arrowroot flour
1 tsp	baking soda
1.5 cup	frozen blue berries
3 tsp	sesame seeds
1/2 tsp	clove powder
1 tbsp	vanilla
1/3 cup	coconut oil
1/3 cup	honey (or less)
Pinch	sea salt

Method
Place ground flax seed in 1.5 cup of boiling water, mix and put aside for 5 minuets.
Combine and mix the ingredients (except blueberries) together, and mix batter to get a thick texture. Let the mixture sit for 1/2 hr.
Preheat oven to 350 degrees.
Mix in blueberries, shape batter into round patties on a baking pan.
Bake on for 20-30 minutes.

Variation
You can use any un-sweetened jam or other berries instead of the blue berries.

Carrot Cake/Muffins

(10-12 servings)

Ingredients

3 tbsp	ground flax seed
3/4 cup	boiling water
1.5 cup	buckwheat flour
3/4 tsp	baking soda (avoid baking powder as it may have corn or potato starch)
1/2 cup	olive oil
1 cup	pitted chopped dates
2 cup	coarsely grated carrots
1 cup	rice milk
1 tbsp	fresh lemon juice
1 tsp	ground cinnamon
3 cm	ginger (finely graded)
1/2 cup	pecans or walnuts
3/4 cup	seedless raisins
1/2 tsp	sea salt

Method

In large bowl stir together ground flax seed, and boiling water and let it sit for 5 minutes. Add flour, rice milk, backing powder and olive oil and whip batter for 5-6 minutes.

Stir in the other ingredients.

Pour into greased pan or a cake pan, and bake at 350 F for 35-40 minutes, or until the top turns brown.

Desserts

Buckwheat Pear Cake

(10 serving)

Ingredients

3 tbsp	ground flax seed
1 cup	boiling water
2 cups	buckwheat flour,
3/4 tsp	baking soda
1 cup	rice milk
1/2 cup	walnuts
1/2 cup	olive oil
3/4 cup	honey (or less)
3	large pears, peeled and cut into chunks
1/2 tsp	sea salt
2 tbsp	rose water
1/4 tsp	nutmeg
1 tsp	ground cinnamon
1/4 tsp	ground cloves (optional)

Method

In large bowl stir together flax seed, and 1 cup of boiling water and let it sit for 5 minutes. Add flour, rice milk, backing powder and olive oil, to the bowl and whip for 5-6 minutes.

Stir in the other ingredients.

Pour into greased pan or a cake pan and bake at 350F for 35-40 minutes.

Variation

For different flavors try substituting pears with other allowed fruits such as mangoes.

For a chocolate flavored cake replace pears with 4 tsp carob powder and add 1/4 cup of ground walnuts, and replace honey with 10 pitted dates chopped to small pieces.

Macaroons

(12-16 serving)

Ingredients

1cup	coconut grind
3tblsp	ground flax seed
1/3cup	boiling Water
1/2 cup (or less)	honey

Method

In large bowl, stir together the ground flax seeds and boiling water, and let it sit for 5 minutes.

Mix in the rest of the ingredients.

Drop small spoonfuls onto oiled baking sheet. Bake at 350F for 20-30 minutes. Chill and enjoy.

Walnut Cookies

Same as macaroons, except replace coconut powder with ground walnut. These cookies have a great earthy taste.

Desserts

Pumpkin Teff cookies

(12-16 serving)
Ingredients

4 tsp	ground flax seed
1/2 cup	boiling water
1.5 cups	teff flour (you can grind the seeds in a coffee grinder flours too)
1 cup	water
2 tsp	arrowroot flour
1 tsp	baking soda
2 cup	pumpkin, shredded
1/4 cup	pumpkin seed
1/4 cup	raisins
1 tbsp	vanilla
1/3 cup	coconut oil
4 tsp	cinnamon powder
1/3 cup (or less)	un-pasteurized honey

Method
Place ground flax seed in 1/2 cup of boiling water, mix and put aside for 5 minuets.
Combine and mix the ingredients together, and mix batter to get a thick texture. Let the mixture sit for 1/2 hr.
Preheat oven to 350F degrees.
Shape batter into 1/3 inch thick cookie on a baking pan.
Bake on for 20 minutes.

Variation
You can use any un-sweetened jam or frozen berries in place of the pumpkins.

Ginger Date Cookies

(10-12 serving)

Ingredients

4 tbsp	ground flax seed
4 tsp	arrow root, powder
2 cup	boiling water
2 cup	quinoa flour
1/2 tsp	baking soda
6 tbsp	ginger, fine graded
20	dates, seeded, chopped
4 tsp	un-pasteurized honey
1/4 cup	olive oil
1/2 tsp	clove, powder
1 tsp	cinnamon powder

Method

Mix ground flax seed and arrowroot powder in boiling water. Let it sit for 5 minuets.

Mix in the rest of the ingredients and stir the batter.

Place spoonfuls on a greased baking pan and bake at 350F, preheated oven for 20-25 minutes.

Rice Crisps

Ingredients

3 cups	puffed brown rice (or millet puffs)
1/2cup	almond nut butter (or pumpkin seed butter)
1/4 cup	rice milk
1 tsp	vanilla extract
1/3 cup	un-pasteurized honey

Method

Cream together rice milk, honey and nut butter over low heat until easily stirred together. Add vanilla stir and take off heat.

Mix in the rice crisps.

Pat down the mixture into a pan. Bake at 350F until golden (20-30 minuets)

Allow to cool, then cut into squares.

Variations

For different flavors try adding, carob powder, cinnamon, or nutmeg, different nuts or nut butter, or seeds, dates, or resins to the mixtures.

PART 5
Scientific Evidence

Scientific Evidence In Support of The Efficacy Of The Hypoallergenic Diet

Dating back to the 1930's, investigators have been studying the effects of The Hypoallergenic Diet on different diseases. Most of these studies involved a relatively small number of individuals. Taken collectively though, these studies shed light on the role of this diet in treatment of diseases. Specifically, they point to the concept of individual variability in food tolerance and food sensitivity.

What follows is a number of select studies pointing to the efficacy of ypoallergenic diet in treatment of specific conditions.

Migraines

In a 1983 study published in The Lancet (a prestigious medical journal) by Egger et al., 88 children suffering from severe, frequent migraines were placed on an hypoallergenic diet. The diet consisted typically of one meat (lamb or chicken), one carbohydrate (rice or potato), one fruit (banana or apple), vegetables (Brassica), water, and vitamin and calcium supplements for 3-4 weeks. If success was not achieved within 3-4 weeks, a second hypoallergenic diet (different foods) was attempted. A recovery rate of 92% was reported. Of the 82 children who improved, 74 developed symptoms upon the re-challenge phase (reintroduction of offending foods to the diet). The most common offending foods were found to be milk 27%, egg 24%, chocolate 22%, orange 21%, and wheat 21%.

In a1993 study published in the journal of Pediatric Medicine, Guariso G and colleagues studied the possible correlation between migraine and food intolerance in 43 patients aged from 7 to 18 years. Half of them (group A) followed a hypoallergenic diet (including 8 simple foods) for 4 weeks. Afterward each patient has been challenged weekly in an open trial, introducing in the diet the different foods and additives previously eliminated. The second half of the patients (group B) were not following any diet. nor a pharmacological prophylaxis, but they have been followed up with a clinical diary. Among the patients on hypoallergenic diet 12 only concluded the trial: 6/12 presented a completed remission of headache, 5/12 had a significant improvement of the migrainous pattern. The food recognized responsible of the attacks were: cacao, banana, egg, hazelnuts.

Arthritis

In 1980, Hicklin et. Al. published an article in the Journal of Clinical Allergy, titled *The effect of diet in rheumatoid arthritis*. In this study Heckling and colleagues administered an hypoallergenic diet to 22 patients with rheumatoid arthritis. Twenty of the patients (91%) reported an improvement in their symptoms.

Beri et. al. prescribed an eliminationand-rechallenge diet to 27 patients with rheumatoid arthritis. In this 1988 study, published in Annals of Rheumatological Diseases, 10 of 14 patients who completed the diet program demonstrated significant clinical improvements.

In another controlled trial published in The Lancet in 1991, 27 patients with rheumatoid arthritis underwent a partial fast, followed by individual food challenges (Kjeldsen-Kragh et. al., 1997). 17 Foods which provoked symptoms were avoided. These foods were animal foods, refined sugar, citrus fruits, preservatives, coffee, tea, alcohol, salt, and strong spices. A control group of 26 patients ate an ordinary diet. After four weeks, the diet group showed a significant improvement in the number of tender joints, Ritchie's articular index, number of swollen joints, pain score, duration of morning stiffness, grip strength, erythrocyte sedimentation rate, and C-reactive protein levels. In the control group, only pain score improved. The benefits in the hypoallergenic diet group were still present after one year.

Irritable bowl syndrome, and inflammatory bowel diseases

In a 1989 study, 189 patients with irritable bowel syndrome consumed an hypoallergenic diet for three weeks. In this study, titled Food Intolerance and the Irritable Bowel Syndrome, Nanda R. and colleagues eliminated dairy products, cereals, citrus fruits, potatoes, tea, coffee, alcohol, additives, and preservatives. Ninety-one patients (48.2%) improved. Subsequent reintroduction phase with individual foods provoked symptoms in 73 of the 91 responders; of these, 72 remained well on a modified diet during a mean follow-up period of 14.7 months.

In another Lancet published study, Riordan and colleagues treated 136 patients with active Crohn's disease with a type of hypoallergenic diet. In this 1993 study, 78 (84%) of the 93 patients who continued the diet for 14 days, achieved clinical remission. Of the patients who followed the diet, 45 percent remained disease-free for at least two years.

Asthma

In a 1977 investigation of 188 children with allergic rhinitis and/or bronchial asthma, Ogle and colleagues achieved complete remission in 62% of children, with partial improvements in an additional 28%. These children were treated solely with the hypoallergenic diet for six weeks. Upon challenge, 40% of the children, who had improved, experienced a recurrence of symptoms.

Hoj et. Al. conducted a double-blind controlled trial of hypoallergenic diet in severe asthma. In this 1981 study 41 patients were randomly assigned an antigen-free Diet, or to a control diet. By the end of two weeks, 9 out of 21 patients consuming the diet showed improvements, compared to 1 out of 16 in the control group.

Other diseases

Similar investigations have shown marked improvements in aphthous ulcers, gallbladder disease, recurrent otitis media, and nephrotic syndrome. Perhaps what is most intriguing is the effect of hypoallergenic diet on mental disorders. At least 6 trials in ADD/ ADHD have demonstrated improvement in 50-75% of children via intervention with hypoallergenic diets.

For a complete list of these studies the reader is recommended to consult the 1998 review article published by Alan R. Gaby titled The Role of Hidden Food Allergy/Intolerance in Chronic Disease by Alan R. Gaby, M.D.

Reference

Part 1

Food sensitivity and GI health
Russell B. Marz, N.D. <u>Medical Nutrition From Marz</u> 2nd Ed. 1997, p.p. 289-311

Auto-Immune manifestation of food sensitivity
Russell B. Marz, N.D, <u>Medical Nutrition From Marz</u> 2nd Ed. 1997, p.p. 289-311

Large bowl flora and food sensitivity
Kjeldsen- Kragh. AJCN. 1999;70 (3suppl): 594S-600S

Adrenal fatigue and food sensitivity
James L. Wilson <u>Adrenal Fatigue: The 21st Century Stress Syndrome</u> p.p. 175-187

Cellular metabolism and food sensitivity
C. Samuel West, DN, ND, <u>The Golden Seven Plus one</u>, 1980

Alternative methods of identifying food Sensitivities
James L. Wilson <u>Adrenal Fatigue: The 21st Century Stress Syndrome</u> p.p. 83-92

Part 2

How the diet is done
1-Adapted from the protocols of the Canadian College of Naturopathic Medicine, Toronto, 2005-2006

2-Phylis Austin, Agatha Thrash M.D. <u>Food Allergies Made Simple</u>, 1992

The rational behind the elimination of main food groups:
Paul Pitchford <u>Healing with whole foods, oriental tradition and modern nutrition</u> 2ND edit. p.194 and p.207-209

Part 5

Scientific evidence
Alan R Gaby, M.D. The Role of Hidden Food Allergy/Intolerance in Chronic Disease (Alt Med Rev 1998; 3(2): 90-100).

Glossary

Acne: Acne is an inflammatory disease of the skin, caused by changes in the structures consisting of a hair roots and sweat gland.

ADD/ADHD: (Attention-deficit hyperactivity disorder (ADHD) (sometimes also referred to as ADD) is a psychiatric diagnosis that identifies hyperactivity, forgetfulness, mood shifts, poor impulse control, and distractibility. ADHD is commonly diagnosed among children.

Adrenal glands: The adrenal glands are triangle-shaped glands that sit atop the kidneys; their name indicates that position (ad: near or at + renes: kidneys). They are chiefly responsible for regulating the stress response.

Allergen: An allergen is a substance that causes the allergic reaction. It can be ingested, inhaled, injected or comes into contact with skin.

Amino acids: the basic building blocks of proteins. Amino acids are divided into essential, or non-essential. The human body cannot make the essential amino acids and it is necessary (essential) to get it through the diet.

Anaphylaxis: Anaphylaxis is a severe and rapid allergic reaction to an allergen. Anaphylactic shock is a life-threatening medical emergency because of rapid constriction of the breathing airway.

Antibody: An antibody is a protein used by the immune system to identify and neutralize foreign objects like bacteria and viruses.

Antigen: An antigen is a substance that stimulates an immune response, especially the production of antibodies. Antigens are usually proteins or polysaccharides on the surface of bacteria and virus cells, but can be any type of molecule, including small molecules attached to other proteins.

Arthritis: Arthritis (from Greek arthro-, joint + -itis, inflammation) is a group of conditions that affect the health of the joints in the body. Arthritic diseases, which are autoimmune diseases, include rheumatoid arthritis and psoriatic arthritis.

ATP: Adenosine 5'-triphosphate (ATP) is the molecule known in biochemistry as the 'molecular currency' of energy transfer; that is, ATP is able to store and transport chemical energy within cells.

Autoimmune reactions: Autoimmune reactions or diseases arise from an overactive immune response of the body against substances and tissues normally present in the body. In other words, the body attacks its own cells.

Glossary

Bile: Bile is a yellow-green detergent like fluid that is made by the liver, stored in the gallbladder and secreted into the duodenum (the beginning part of the small intestine) where it functions in allowing fat and water to mix and assists in the absorption of fats

Bowel flora: In microbiology, flora refers to the collective bacteria and other microorganisms in an ecosystem. Bowel flora refers to the flora within the small and mostly large intestine.

Brain-gut axis: The continuous bi-directional flow of information and feedback that takes place between the gastrointestinal tract, and the brain and spinal cord.

Cortisol: Cortisol is a corticosteroid hormone that is involved in the response to stress; it increases blood pressure and blood sugar levels and suppresses the immune system.

Corticosteroids: In physiology, corticosteroids are a class of steroid hormones that are produced in the adrenal gland. Synthetic glucocorticoids are used in the treatment of inflammatory and autoimmune diseases.

Circadian rhythm: The 'internal body clock' that regulates the (roughly) 24-hour cycle of biological processes in animals and plants.

Chronic: Symptoms occurring over a long period of time

Chronic fatigue: Is a syndrome of unknown and possibly multiple etiology, affecting the central nervous system (CNS), and immune system. Often symptoms such as pain, muscle weakness, hypersensitivity, digestive disturbances, and depression accompany an extremely low stamina that unlike natural fatigue is not responsive to rest.

Crohn's Disease: Is a chronic inflammatory disease of the digestive tract and it can involve any part of it, from the mouth to the anus. It typically affects the large bowel and is often associated with autoimmune disorders outside the bowel.

Dermatitis: Dermatitis is a term literally meaning 'inflammation of the skin'. It is usually used to refer to eczema. There are several different types. Usually all of them have in common an allergic reaction to specific allergens.

Detoxification: In general is the removal of toxic substances from the body. It is one of the functions of the liver and kidneys, but can also be achieved by specific diets, hydrotherapy, or artificially via techniques such as dialysis and medication.

Glossary

Enteric Nervous System (ENS): Autonomic nervous system within the walls of the digestive tract. The ENS regulates digestion and peristalsis.

Eczema: An acute or chronic inflammation of the skin, characterized by redness, itching, and the outbreak of oozing lesions, which become crusted and scaly.

Enzymes: Proteins that act as a catalysts in mediating and speeding a specific chemical reaction. Enzymes are specific to the reaction they participate in.

Etiology: Etiology is the study of causation. In medicine in particular, the term means the occurrences, reasons, and variables causing the disease.

Epithelium: The inner and outer tissue covering digestive tract organs.

Erythrocyte Sedimentation Rate: A laboratory technique measuring the viscosity of blood. It can be used to correlate allergenic responses.

Ferment: Fermentation refers to the process can also refer to bacterial metabolic breakdown of nutrient molecules in the absence of air.

Gall bladder: The gallbladder is a pear-shaped organ that stores about 50 ml of bile. It is connected to the liver and the duodenum by the bile tract.

Gout: Gout is a form of arthritis caused by the accumulation of uric acid crystals in joints. It is an intensely painful disease, which most commonly affects the big toe.

Hypothesis: A hypothesis is a proposed explanation for a phenomenon. A scientific hypothesis must be testable and based on previous observations or extensions of scientific theories.

Hormone: A hormone (from Greek horman – 'to set in motion') is a chemical messenger from one cell or organ to another. Hormone actions vary widely, but can include stimulation or inhibition of growth, regulating metabolism, and activation or inhibition of the immune system preparation for a new activity.

IBS: Irritable bowel syndrome (IBS) is a group of functional bowel disorders which involve cyclical bouts of diarrhea and constipation.

IgE: IgE is an antibody. IgE plays a role in immediate allergenic reactions and the defense against parasites such as worms.

Glossary

Immune system: The immune system is the system of specialized cells and organs that protect an organism from outside biological influences. When the immune system is functioning properly, it protects the body against bacteria and viral infections, destroying cancer cells and foreign substances.

Inflammation: Inflammation is the first response of the immune system to infection or irritation. Inflammation is characterized by redness, heat, swelling, pain, and dysfunction of the organs or tissue involved.

Lumen: the inside of a tube. For example the intestinal lumen would be the area inside the intestine.

Lymphatic System: The lymphatic system acts as a secondary circulatory system. Lymph originates as blood fluid lost from the circulatory system. The lymphatic system returns it to the circulatory system.

Membrane Potential: Membrane potential is the electrical potential difference (voltage) across a cell's membrane.

Metabolic rate: Is a measure of all biochemical processes of an organism. The cell metabolism includes all chemical processes in a cell.

Migraine: Migraine is the most common type of vascular headache. Migraine headaches are usually characterized by severe pain on one or both sides of the head, an upset stomach, and at times disturbed vision.

Mitochondria: Mitochondria are sometimes described as 'cellular power plants' because their primary function is to convert organic materials into energy in the form of ATP.

Mucosa: Mucosa or the mucus membrane is the inner lining of internal organs of the body and are involved in absorption and digestion.

Pancreas: A digestive organ that secretes enzymes into the small intestine that are involved in protein, CHO and fat breakdown

Parasympathetic nervous system: The parasympathetic nervous system is one of two divisions of the autonomic nervous system. It conserves energy as it slows the heart rate, increases intestinal and gland activity.

Glossary

Peristalsis: Contraction of circular and longitudinal muscles lining the gastrointestinal (GI) system Functions to move a bolus of food along the digestive system

Psoriasis: Psoriasis is a condition whose main symptom is gray or silvery flaky patches on the skin which are red and inflamed underneath. Commonly affected areas include the scalp, elbows, knees, arms, stomach and back. Psoriasis is autoimmune in origin, and is not contagious.

Rhinitis: Rhinitis describes irritation and inflammation of the nose. Symptoms include a runny nose, sneezing, congestion and irritation in the nose, eyes, throat and ears.

Randomized placebo control trial: describes an especially stringent way of conducting an experiment, usually on human subjects, in attempt to eliminate subjective bias on the part of both experimental subjects and the experimenters. A control group is an experimental group receiving no treatment. This is essential to help rule out effects imagined or effects that will just happen at random.

Sympathetic Nervous System: SNS activates what is often termed the 'fight or flight' or the stress response, which activates the secretion of adrenal gland.

SLE: Systemic Lupus Erythematosus is an autoimmune disorder in which antibodies are created against the patient's own DNA. It can cause various symptoms relate to the skin, kidney, joints, blood and immune system.

Titers (antibody): A titer is the unit in which the detection of many substances is expressed. Antibody titer is a test is performed on a diluted blood sample to detected the amount of antibodies present in the sample.

Ulcerative Colitis: Ulcerative Colitis is an inflammatory disease of the bowel that usually affects the distal end of the large intestine and rectum and has chronic diarrhea (sometimes bloody) as a characteristic symptom. Other symptoms may include abdominal pain and discomfort, bloating, and nausea.

Urticaria: Urticaria or hives is an allergic reaction that causes raised red skin welts. Urticaria is also known as nettle rash. Urticaria is generally caused by direct contact with an allergen.

Villi: Villi are tiny, finger-like structures that protrude from the wall of the intestine and have additional extensions called microvili. These serve to increase the absorptive surface area of the intestine.

Resources

Web Sites:

Hypoallergenic Diet:

www.hypoallergenicdiet.com

Gluten-Free Recipes:

www.recipegoldmine.com/glutenfree/glutenfree.html
www.glutenfree.com/recipes.htm
hwww.recipesource.com/special-diets/gluten-free/
http://lesleycooks.tripod.com/glutenfree/glutenfree.htm#soup

Dairy-Free Recipes:

www.recipezaar.com/r/5
www.truestarhealth.com/Notes/2406000.html

Sugar Free Diet:

www.lifeclinic.com/whatsnew/cookbook/diabetescookbook.asp

Vegan Recipes:

http://vegweb.com/recipes/
www.vegancooking.com/
www.vrg.org/recipes/
www.vegsource.com/recipe/

Resources

Books:

Health and Nutrition:

Healing With Whole Foods, Oriental Tradition And Modern Nutrition, Paul Pitchford

Adrenal Fatigue: The 21st Century Stress Syndrome, James L. Wilson

Food Allergies Made Simple, 1992 Phylis Austin, Agatha Thrash M.D.

The Golden Seven Plus one, 1980, Samuel West, DN, ND,

Hypothyroidism, The Unsuspected Illness, Broada Barness

Health and Mental, Emotional Balance:

Staying Well With Guided Imagery, How To Harness The Power Of Your Imagination for Health And Healing, Belleruth Naparstek

Anatomy Of The Spirit, The Seven Stages Of Power And Healing, Caroline Myss, Ph.D.

Power Vs Force: An Anatomy of Consciousness, David Hawkins, M.D., Ph.D.

Food Elimination Charts:

For three to six weeks consume only the allowed foods, and avoid others. (Your Naturopathic or Medical Doctor may recommend further restriction to reflect your specific symptoms and medical history)

Vegetables:	
Consume	❑ All fresh vegetables (try to incorporate all vegetables such as asparagus, Brussels sprouts, celery, cauliflower, cabbage onions, garlic, carrots, beets, leeks, green beans, broccoli, leafy greens – kale, mustard greens, turnip greens, bok choy, watercress etc.) ❑ Sweet potatoes, Yams, Squash, Pumpkin, (Very soothing on the GI) ❑ Sprouts: sunflower sprouts, pea and bean sprouts (esp. alfalfa & red clover as they help with detoxification)
Avoid	❑ Tomatoes, corn, mushrooms, green peppers, red pepper, bell peppers, potatoes ❑ If ragweed allergy present then eliminate artichokes, iceberg lettuce, sunflower seeds, dandelion, chamomile and chicory.

Fruits:	
Consume	❑ All fresh/frozen fruits (see exceptions below) ❑ All berries fresh or frozen (except strawberries) ❑ All jams and fruit sauces of allowed fruits (with no sugars or preservatives added)
Avoid	❑ Bananas (are often treated with ripening chemicals) ❑ Citrus (oranges, grapefruit, and any citric acid containing beverage) ❑ Melons (often contain and promote mold growth) ❑ Strawberries ❑ Peaches and apricots ❑ Apples ❑ Dried fruits (does not include dates, organic-sulfite free raisins, sulfite free-figs, or unsweetened dried sulfite free cranberries)

143

Grains and Cereals:		
Consume	❑	Brown rice, rice, millet, buckwheat, quinoa, tapioca, teff, amaranth
	❑	Pasta, cereals and pastry made from these grains.
Avoid	❑	All gluten-containing grains (wheat, spelt, rye, oats, barley) and breads, pasta & other products from flour of these

Legumes and Lentils:		
Consume	❑	All legumes: beans and lentils (all beans, fresh/frozen/dried)
	❑	All peas (fresh/frozen/dried)
Avoid	❑	Soy beans & soy products (tofu, soy milk, soy sauce, miso, tempeh, TVP)
	❑	Soy is another common allergen.

Nuts and seeds:		
Consume	❑	Raw almonds, walnuts, sesame seeds, pumpkin seeds, sunflower seeds
	❑	
Avoid	❑	Peanuts, pistachios, cashews, brazil nuts, hazelnuts
	❑	Any nuts or seeds that are salted or flavored in some way

Animal products:		
Consume	❑	Free-range chicken & turkey breast (best if organic)
	❑	Lamb (best if organic)
	❑	Wild game
	❑	Wild Fish of any kind (except Shark, Swordfish, King mackerel, and Tilefish)
	❑	Farmed organic fish
Avoid	❑	Red meats (beef, pork, bacon), processed meats (hotdogs, salami, wieners, sausage, canned meats, smoked meats) these all contain flower additives and coloring and preservatives
	❑	Dairy (milk, cream, sour cream, cheese, butter, yogurt)
	❑	Eggs
	❑	Sea food: Shell-fish, Shrimp, Lobster, Scallops, Crab
	❑	Catfish, Shark, Swordfish, King mackerel, and Tilefish
	❑	Farmed Inorganic Fish

Oils:		
Consume	❏	Virgin olive oil, cold or with low heat cooking
	❏	Coconut oil for high heat cooking
	❏	Cold pressed sunflower oil, sesame oil, and flax oil for dressing and no heat recipes
Avoid	❏	All other oils
	❏	Refined oils, margarine, shortening

Condiments:		
Consume	❏	Sea salt
	❏	All herbs (e.g. parsley, coriander, watercress, dill, basil, thyme, oregano, garlic, ginger)
	❏	Most spices (e.g. turmeric, fennel, cinnamon, black pepper)
	❏	Spreads: nut/seed butters (e.g. almond, sesame (tahini), sunflower), bean dips (e.g. hummus)
	❏	Sauces: pesto, mustard w/ no additives
	❏	Apple cider/ brown rice vinegar
	❏	Sweeteners: stevia (green/brown, unprocessed) and un-pasteurized honey in moderation.
Avoid	❏	Regular table salt (table salt is not necessarily a food allergen, it just does not have the added minerals and benefits of sea salt)
	❏	Avoid peppers from the nightshade family (Cayenne pepper, red pepper, paprika, jalapeno, curry mix)
	❏	All sweeteners (corn/ brown rice/ maple syrups, molasses, brown/ white sugar, glucose, maltose, maltodextrose, etc.) This includes desserts & all processed foods high in sugars.
	❏	MSG
	❏	All food additives, preservatives, and coloring.

Drinks:	
Consume	❑ Filtered water, at least 6-8 glasses/day ❑ 100% fresh fruit & fresh vegetable juices ❑ (Herbal teas: roobois tea, peppermint, nettle leaf tea, chamomile, licorice root, passion flower, dandelion, milk thistle, and any other herbal tea) ❑ Green tea ❑ Rice milk (unsweetened) ❑ Nut milks (unsweetened)
Avoid	❑ Caffeinated beverages (coffee, black tea, soda) (green tea is an exception) ❑ Alcohol ❑ Dairy (milk & other dairy products) ❑ Soy milk ❑ All fruit drinks high in refined sugar and added sugar ❑ All vegetable drinks high in salt

Food Challenge List:

Challenge (reintroduce) these foods one item at a time. Each Challenge item should be consumed at least two portions a day, on two consecutive days and symptoms should be monitored for a total of three days. If symptoms are present after the first consumption, there is no need to consume the food for two consecutive days. When symptoms are present you should wait until they resolves before challenging the next food.

If you don't generally consume, or know that you will not have any of the listed items in the future there is no point challenging it. Simply move on to the next item.

1	Milk,	23	Potatoes
2	Cream, Ice cream, Sour cream	24	Oranges,
3	Cheese	25	Grapefruit
4	Yogurt	26	Mushrooms
5	Butter	27	All Sea food, Shellfish and Catfish
6	Wheat	28	Peanuts
7	Rye	29	Pistachios
8	Oats	30	Cashews
9	Barley	31	Hazelnuts
10	Spelt	32	All sweeteners (corn/ brown rice/ maple syrups, molasses, brown/ white sugar, etc.)
11	Soy beans	33	Caffeinated beverages (coffee, black tea, soda)
12	Soy milk	34	Chocolate
13	Fermented soy products (tofu, soy sauce, miso, tempeh, TVP)	35	Strawberries
14	Beef	36	Bananas
15	Pork, Bacon	37	Apples
16	Eggs	38	Melons
17	Corn Products	39	Dried fruits
18	Processed meats.	40	All other eliminated foods, one item at a time
19	Bell Peppers		
20	Tomatoes		
21	Eggplant		
22	Red pepper, and other hot peppers		